THERE IS NO CLIMATE CRISIS

What if there is no climate crisis? What if the Earth isn't overheating? What if sea levels aren't rising? What if the world's ice caps aren't melting? What if the polar bears are thriving? What if the weather is becoming less extreme? What if an improving climate is greening the Earth? What if there is no need to reduce CO_2 emissions as they have little to no effect on our planet's climate?

Using 150 years of newspaper articles, temperature charts which have been doctored or even deleted, CIA reports and even letters to U.S. presidents and the Secretary General of the UN, *THERE IS NO CLIMATE CRISIS* reveals that in a futile attempt to fight the non-existent threat of man-made global warming, or climate change, or climate emergency, or climate crisis, or climate extinction or whatever it's called this month, we in the West are about to commit the most expensive and disastrous scientific and economic blunder in human history.

David Craig has written 10 other controversial current affairs books exposing dishonesty, incompetence, stupidity, greed and waste in government, the EU, the private sector, financial services and Britain's bloated charity industry. These include:

THE GREAT UNIVERSITY CON:
How we broke our universities and betrayed a generation

THE GREAT CHARITY SCANDAL:
What really happens to the billions we give to good causes

DON'T BUY IT!
Tricks and traps salespeople use and how to beat them

GREED UNLIMITED:
How David Cameron protects the elites while squeezing the rest of us

PILLAGED:
How they are looting £413 million a day from your savings and pensions . . . and what to do about it

FLEECED!
How we've been betrayed by the politicians, bureaucrats and bankers

THE GREAT EUROPEAN RIP-OFF

SQUANDERED:
How Gordon Brown is wasting over one trillion pounds of our money

PLUNDERING THE PUBLIC SECTOR

RIP-OFF:
The scandalous inside story of the management consulting money machine

THERE IS NO CLIMATE CRISIS

David Craig

ORIGINAL BOOK COMPANY

This edition first published in 2021
The Original Book Company
21b Knyveton Road
Bournemouth BH1 3QQ
United Kingdom

Tel: 07891-745050
david.craig54@yahoo.co.uk

ISBN-13: 978-1-872188-17-1 (paperback)
ISBN: 978-1-872188-18-8 (ebook)

The further a society drifts from the truth,
the more it will hate those that speak it.

– George Orwell

Contents

Thanks to Tony Heller

This book has been inspired by the wonderful work of Tony Heller and his team who run the *Real Climate Science* website. For over 13 years, Tony Heller's brilliant research has exposed the exaggeration, dishonesty and deliberate fraud of the climate catastrophists.

Much of the material in *THERE IS NO CLIMATE CRISIS* comes from Tony Heller's *Real Climate Science* website. I hope I have done justice to his amazing forensic skills and unrelenting search after the truth.

We were warned 150 years ago

In a newspaper article written in 1871, we were warned about how meteorologists, scientists and (often self-proclaimed) climate prophets would inevitably claim that each month, season, year or decade was the warmest, coldest, wettest, driest or stormiest ever known:

THE BRISBANE COURIER, TUESDAY, JANUARY 10, 1871.

IMAGINARY CHANGES OF CLIMATE.

(Pall Mall Gazette.)

THREE consecutive years of drought, while they have stimulated the inventive resources of practical agriculturists, have had the natural effect of calling forth a plentiful crop of speculation from weather prophets, and projectors, and half-instructed meteorologists, and all the philosophic tribe of Laputa in general, to whom the periodical press now affords such fatal facilities. We have often noticed that in the tabular statements of those compilers of weather records who write to the *Times*, useful and welcome as their communications are, every season is sure to be "extraordinary," almost every month one of the driest or wettest, or windiest, coldest or hottest, ever known. Much observation, which ought to correct a tendency to exaggerate, seems in some minds to have rather a tendency to increase it. And many

'Three consecutive years of drought, while they have stimulated the inventive resources of practical agriculturists, have had the natural effect of calling forth a plentiful crop of speculation from weather prophets, and projectors, and half-instructed meteorologists, and all the philosophic tribe of Laputa* in general, to whom the periodical press now affords such fatal facilities.

[. . .]

'We have often noticed that in the tabular statements of those compilers of weather records who write to the *Times*, useful and welcome as their communications are, every season is sure to be "extraordinary", almost every month one of the driest or wettest or windiest, coldest, or hottest ever known. Much observation, which ought to correct a tendency to exaggerate, seems in some minds to have rather a tendency to increase it.'

---

* Laputa is an imaginary flying island described in Jonathan Swift's 1726 satire *Gulliver's Travels*. Laputans are described as becoming so lost in thought that they cannot focus their attention on a conversation or avoid running into a tree or falling into a ditch unless periodically struck by a bladder full of pebbles or dry peas carried by one or two "flappers" or, in their native language, "climenoles", hired for the purpose.

Crisis? What crisis?

In his 2021 book *HOW TO AVOID A CLIMATE DISASTER*, multi-billionaire owner of several private jets and one of the world's richest men, Bill Gates, warned us of the need to halt disastrous man-made global warming – Catastrophic Anthropogenic Global Warming (CAGW):

> 'To stop the warming and avoid the worst effects of climate change – and these effects will be very bad – humans need to stop adding greenhouse gases to the atmosphere.'

Mr Gates was just the latest in a long line of preachy billionaires, climate scientists (both real and self-proclaimed), headline-hungry journalists, attention-seeking Holywood celebrities, UN bureau-crats, climate activists, anti-capitalists, truant schoolchildren and often scientifically-illiterate politicians to use the threat of supposedly 'catastrophic' climate change to terrify us ordinary people into allowing ever more restrictions on our freedoms in order to 'save the planet.'

THE 1920S AND 1930S GLOBAL WARMING SCARE

About a hundred years ago, excited scientists and hyperventilating journalists were warning us that global warming could have disastrous consequences for life on earth:

'North Pole melting. Many glaciers vanished.'

– *Daily Mercury*, 7 April 1923

'Will melting icebergs engulf the world?'

– *Sunday Journal* and *Star*, 13 April 1931

'Hottest summer in 4,000 years,'   – *New York Times*, 2 July 1931

'World heating up. Ice dissolving at Poles. Sea will rise 40 feet.'

– *Cairns Post*, 3 February 1934

'Greenland's glaciers melting, says scientist.'

– *Harrisburg Sunday Courier*, 17 December 1939

'Ice in Arctic melting rapidly.'

– *Hartford Courant Magazine*, 13 October 1940

'Glaciers icebergs melt as the world gets warmer.'

– *The Herald Saturday Magazine*, 29 September 1951

THE 1960S AND 1970S GLOBAL COOLING SCARE

Then by the 1950s the Earth stopped warming and started cooling. Soon all the climate experts and journalists were predicting a catastrophic new Ice Age that would ravage agriculture, lead to food shortages and famine and might even result in wars:

'Scientists agree world is colder.'

       – *New York Times*, 30 January 1961

'Scientist predicts a new Ice Age by 21st century.'

       – *Boston Globe*, 16 April 1970

In 1972, a group of America's leading climatologists wrote a letter to the then President Nixon warning that:

'The present rate of the cooling seems fast enough to bring glacial temperatures in about a century.'

       – Letter to the President, 3 December 1972

'The Earth is cooling. Return of Ice Age is feared.'

       – *Iowa City Press*, 14 April 1973

'Space satellites show new Ice Age coming fast.'

       – *Guardian*, 29 January 1974

'B-r-r-r: New Ice Age on way soon?'

       – *Chicago Tribune*, 2 March 1975

'Ice age coming? Chilling thought for humanity.'

       – *Chicago Tribune*, 2 June 1975

By 1976, even the U.S. CIA started worrying about the effects of a long period of global cooling that could last for centuries:

'Major climatic changes will bring about global unrest of a proportion almost beyond comprehension heightening the risk of international conflict according to a Central Intelligence Agency report released today . . . The adverse weather is likely to last for at least 40 years and possibly for centuries the report said.'

— *Daily News*, 4 May 1976

'International team of specialists finds no end in sight to 30-year cooling trend in Northern hemisphere.'

— *New York Times*, 5 January 1978

'Alarming forecasts made by the CIA. If the cooling trend of the 1960s and 1970s is maintained as most climatologists expect, we shall see more bad harvests, more crop failures, more hunger and probably more famine.'   — *Calgary Herald*, 10 May 1979

'New Ice Age may soon grip cooling Earth.'

— *Sunday Dispatch*, 9 March 1980

'Scientists now blame recurring droughts and floods on a global cooling trend that could trigger massive tragedies for mankind.'

— *Chicago Tribune*, 25 November 1981

TODAY'S GLOBAL WARMING SCARE

Fortunately for all of us, the cooling seemed to stop in the mid 1980s and the Earth started warming again. This new warming led to today's catastrophic anthropogenic global warming climate scare:

'A senior environmental official at the United Nations, Noel Brown, says entire nations could be wiped off the face of the earth by rising sea levels if global warming is not reversed by the year 2000.'   — *Mercury News*, 30 June 1989

'Nuclear conflict, mega-droughts, famine and widespread rioting will spread across the world . . . deaths from war and famine run into the millions, until the planet's population is reduced by such an extent the Earth can cope.' – *Observer*, 11 November 2004

'Climate change study predicts refugees fleeing into Antarctica.'
– *Daily Telegraph*, 13 October 2008

'Barack Obama has only four years to save the world. That is the stark assessment of NASA scientist and leading climate expert Jim Hansen.' – *Guardian*, 18 January 2009

'The best scientific projections indicate that we have very little time left – indeed less than 100 months – in which to alter our behaviour drastically.' – The UK Prince of Wales, 26 May 2009

'Four years to save the Earth: 2020 is the deadline to avert climate catastrophe, experts claim.' – *Daily Mail*, 29 June 2017

'The planet is getting warmer in catastrophic ways. And fear may be the only thing that saves us,' – *New York Times*, February 2019

'Climate change is the number one issue facing humanity. And it's the number one issue for me. Unchecked it's actually going to bake this planet.' – President Joe Biden, 21 March 2021

IS THERE REALLY A CLIMATE CRISIS?

Just because the experts and journalists and politicians got things utterly wrong in the global warming scare of the 1920s and 1930s and then got it totally wrong yet again in the global cooling scare of the 1960s and 1970s, it doesn't mean they've got it wrong again this time with today's CAGW scare. But given that the scientists and journalists and politicians have twice completely misunderstood the Earth's climate and made predictions that turned out to be ludicrously inaccurate, one might expect a small degree of humility from them with their latest climate scare – the CAGW extinction of mankind scare.

One might expect our climate-alarmist scientists to admit that they believe that there is man-made global warming due mainly to rising atmospheric CO_2 levels, but they can't be sure. One might expect them to say that they were continuing to study the various influences on the Earth's climate to either confirm or adjust their predictions. One might expect them to state that they were still open to counter-arguments and quite prepared to look at any evidence that contradicted their theory of CO_2-caused CAGW. And, as one doom-laden prediction after another turned out to be hopelessly inaccurate, we might have expected the alarmists to tone down their catastrophist rhetoric and stop trying to terrify us with their doom-and-disaster scenarios which just weren't happening.

But strangely, we seem to be seeing exactly the opposite. Instead of admitting that they can't be certain about CO_2-driven climate change, today's CAGW scientists are insisting that anyone who doesn't accept their theory is a 'denier' – suggesting that 'climate deniers' are on the same moral level as Holocaust deniers. Worse still, anyone who dares express doubts about the new CO2-fuelled CAGW religion is treated like a blasphemer or heretic and is viciously attacked, deplatformed and cancelled. Often they will also soon find an outraged cyber-pitchfork-wielding Twitter mob, or even a real mob, demanding they retract their opinions, apologise for them and prostrate themselves to the vengeance-seeking CAGW activists. Several well-respected climate scientists have even lost their jobs for daring to express doubts about the CAGW dogma.

In September 2015, a group of climate alarmists wrote to the then president Obama and to the U.S. Attorney General demanding that any individuals who questioned whether CO2-fuelled CAGW was really happening should be prosecuted using the RICO (Racketeer Influenced and Corrupt Organizations) Act for allegedly having: *'knowingly deceived the American people about the risks of climate change'.*

Today's CAGW catastrophists are behaving more like religious zealots obsessed with forcing their version of the truth on us and burning any heretics rather than being objective scientists continually searching for a better understanding of the highly complex thermodynamic system that is the Earth's climate.

In *THERE IS NO CLIMATE CRISIS*, I will use newspaper reports from more than 150 years as well as temperature charts that have been doctored or even deleted and new scientific discoveries to demolish all the apocalyptic disaster scenarios of the CAGW alarmists.

THERE IS NO CLIMATE CRISIS will show that the alarmists' claims of an overheating planet, supposedly melting ice caps, rapidly-rising sea levels, soon-to-be-extinct polar bears, increasing heatwaves and wildfires, more and worse hurricanes, worsening droughts, impending crop failures and famines have absolutely no basis in reality. Moreover, the book will expose how, when the Earth's climate repeatedly, and almost mockingly, failed to follow the predictions made by the CAGW alarmists, the alarmists started falsifying data, lied about the number of scientists who actually supported their theory of mainly CO_2-driven CAGW and tried to destroy the reputations and careers of the many scientists who doubted the beliefs of the alarmists' CAGW doomsday cult.

As the world emerges from the disastrous economic shock of the Chinese Wuhan Covid-19 pandemic, which has killed millions and impoverished tens of millions, we need to create economic growth and millions of jobs.

Energy prices in the West are now four to five times as expensive as prices in China and India as the West rushes to close down cheap, reliable coal and gas-fired power stations and tries to replace them with expensive and unreliable solar and wind power in the mistaken belief that this will somehow 'save the planet'. If we carry on like this, soon our energy prices will be up to ten times more expensive than in the rest of the world. We are wilfully creating an economic disaster which will make Western companies uncompetitive and destroy jobs in the West as they are moved to countries with lower energy prices. This will make a post-pandemic economic revival impossible.

Meanwhile, our economic rivals look on with amusement and even bewilderment as we enthusiastically sabotage our own economies and destroy millions of jobs. We are probably committing the greatest act of self-harm in human history in the deluded belief that human activities are somehow causing catastrophic climate change.

In *THERE IS NO CLIMATE CRISIS*, I hope I can help warn people of the coming disaster we are needlessly inflicting on ourselves. Then we can put pressure on our scientifically-ignorant, posturing, virtue-signalling politicians to stop leading us into unnecessary societal and economic suicide.

PART I

We've been here before

'Future generations will wonder in bemused amazement that the early 21st Century's developed world went into hysterical panic over a globally averaged temperature increase of a few tenths of a degree and, on the basis of gross exaggerations of highly uncertain computer projections combined into implausible chains of inference, proceeded to contemplate a roll-back of the industrial age.'

– Professor Richard Lindzen

CHAPTER I

The 1920s/1930s Global Warming scare

In the sixty or so years between the 1880s and 1940s the Earth's temperature warmed by anywhere between 0.5°C and 1°C. There was very limited global temperature monitoring at the time, so we don't have an exact or reliable figure. But most scientists are in general agreement that there was a 60-year warming period.

During this time there were a series of disastrous global heatwaves. In 1911, for example, there were thousands of deaths from the heat in Germany, Britain, France and the U.S.:

**THE BENDIGO INDEPENDENT,
FRIDAY, AUGUST 11, 1911;**

TERRIBLE HEAT WAVE.

OVER 1000 DEATHS IN GERMANY.
BERLIN, Wednesday, August 9.
Upwards of 1000 deaths from sunstroke have occurred in different parts of Germany as a result of the terrific heat wave that has prevailed during the past ten days.

In many cases people who went bathing to obtain relief from the intense heat died of heart failure.

In the valley of the Moselle an epidemic of disease has been caused by decaying fish, which had been netted in shoals. The fish were suffering from a kind of scrofula, due to the overheated state of the water.

In many cities the water supply is available for only two hours daily, and then only for drinking purposes. Even in Berlin street watering has had to be suspended.

Typhus fever and gastritis have been caused in many places through the impaired quality of the water supplied for domestic purposes.

Ice also is running short, and chemists who are ordinarily bound to supply this summer luxury, are now selling it only on the production of a doctor's certificate.

GREAT HEAT IN ENGLAND.
PARIS, Wednesday, August 9.
Severe heat is still being felt in England, the thermometer registering 95 degrees in the shade in London to-day.

Last month was the most rainless July experienced in England for the past 50 years.

LARGE NUMBERS OF DEATHS IN PARIS.
PARIS, Wednesday, August 9.
Owing to a heat-wave in Paris 588 deaths above the normal number have occurred during the past fortnight.

HEAT AND DROUGHT IN AMERICA.
NEW YORK, Thursday, Aug. 10.
The intense heat and drought are seriously affecting the corn and wheat growing areas of the United States.

In Germany, many people died from sunstroke. Others died from heart failure when they tried to cool off in rivers and lakes. There was a typhus epidemic and people could only buy ice if they had a doctor's certificate. Just in Paris, it was estimated that several thousand people died from heat-related causes. And in the United States, temperatures hit record highs, thermometers burst and there were deaths from heat and suicide:

The Tribune-Republican

SCRANTON, PA., TUESDAY, JULY 4, 1911.

NATION IN THROES OF HEAT TIDE

Government Forecasters in Washington Predict Most Oppressively Hot and Sweltering "Fourth" in Decade With No Relief in Sight Unless Through Local Rain.

TEMPERATURE RECORDS BROKEN AT ALL POINTS

Suicides, Deaths and Prostrations Reported in Many Cities—Thermometers Burst

ALL HEAT RECORDS IN NEW ENGLAND BROKEN

BOSTON, July 3.—All heat records of the weather bureau were shattered by the hot wave which encircled New England today. Three deaths and more than fifty prostrations were reported in Boston and its suburbs alone, while scores of people in other parts of New England were overcome. The White mountains of New Hampshire, famed for their cooling breezes, offered little relief, for at some points the mercury registered ninety-six in the shade. At Burlington, Vt., the weather bureau reported temperature of 100, exceeding by four degrees the highest mark reached during the seventy years that local records have been kept.

In Boston the official mark was 102, reached at 3 o'clock in the afternoon. This was half a degree hotter than the record of Sept. 7, 1881, the highest ever before recorded by the weather bureau.

DEATHS AND SUICIDE TOLL IN BALTIMORE.

BALTIMORE, Md., July 3.—The hot weather took heavy toll here today, although the official maximum temperature of ninety-five degrees was two degrees lower than that of yesterday. Three deaths, one of them a suicide, two attempts at suicide and six prostrations were reported as a result of the heat.

F. Halvorse, machinist's mate on the United States torpedoboat destroyer Monaghan, which was sent here to take part in tomorrow's marine pa-

There was another deadly global heatwave in 1921, with temperatures surpassing those of 1911 to hit a new 50-year record level:

The New York Times

MONDAY, OCTOBER 3, 1921

FREAK WEATHER LAID TO EARTHLY MUMPS

"Old Spheroid" Convalescing, Say Diagnosticians, But Fever Clings With Abnormal Heat.

NEW RECORD FOR 50 YEARS

Many Disasters of Recent Months Ascribed to High Temperatures and Lack of Moisture.

By The Associated Press.
The old spheroid known as the earth is emerging from what some human diagnosticians might call a severe attack of meteorological mumps. It has been accompanied by an intermittent fever, manifested in a world-wide heat wave of unusual length and intensity. In spite of crises and relapses—earthquakes, tidal waves, cloudbursts, typhoons, waterspouts, hailstorms, floods and hurricanes in many widely separat-

By 1922 the U.S. Commerce Department reported that:

'The Arctic ocean is warming up, icebergs are growing scarce and in some places the seals are finding the waters too hot.'[1]

By 1923, with more hot weather and more polar ice melting, leading scientists were asking: 'Is the North Pole going to melt entirely?' And experts were coming to the conclusion that the Earth was experiencing:

'A radical change in climatic conditions with hitherto unheard-of high temperatures on that part of the earth's surface.'

DAILY MERCURY:
APRIL 7, 1923.

NORTH POLE MELTING.

MANY GLACIERS VANISHED.

Is the North Pole going to melt entirely? Are the Artic regions warming up, with the prospect of a great climatic change in that part of the world?

Science is asking these questions (says "Popular Science Siftings"). Reports from fishermen, seal hunters, and explorers who sail the seas around Spitzbergen and the eastern Arctic all point to a radical change in climatic conditions, with hitherto unheard-of high temperatures on that part of the earth's surface

The idea that the planet was warming seemed to be confirmed by observations in Switzerland where 81 of 100 glaciers studied were retreating, 4 were stable and only 15 had increased:

THE COURIER-MAIL, BRISBANE, FRIDAY, JUNE 22, 1934.

EARTH GROWING WARMER

What Swiss Glaciers Reveal

GENEVA, June 20.
Apropos of the world-wide drought, scientific observation of the Swiss glaciers indicates that the earth is gradually growing warmer and drier. Only fifteen of 100 glaciers were observed last year to have increased; four remained stationary; and 81 decreased.

In the North, the summer sea temperature around Spitzbergen reached 28°C (82.4°F) – massively above its normal level of just 5°C (41°F). And at the South Pole there was even a heatwave in Antarctica where temperatures reached 25°C (77°F) twice in just a few weeks:

THE WEST AUSTRALIAN, THURSDAY, JUNE 7, 1934.

ANTARCTIC HEAT WAVE.

Explorers Puzzled But Pleased.

LITTLE AMERICA, June 5.—This little polar community—Rear-Admiral Byrd's American expedition to the antarctic—has entered on the 14th day of what for want of a better description, might be called "the hottest winter heat wave in the memory of the oldest inhabitants."

At 8 o'clock this morning the temperature had soared to 25 degrees above zero To add to the complexity, a blizzard is bringing soft moist snow out of the east, which is almost like rain.

The warm spell is a boon to the expedition's tractor department, which is busy overhauling three machines. Handling metal at low temperatures is cruel work, and the men are glad the cold has moderated.

In 1934 two experts (a polar explorer and a leading authority on the effect of Polar conditions on the climate) suggested:

'The world is gradually becoming both warmer and drier. One day the great Polar icecaps may melt – raising the level of the oceans from 40 to 50 feet (12 to 15 metres), and wiping half of England off the map.'

THE CAIRNS POST, FEBRUARY 3, 1934.

"WORLD HEATING UP."

"ICE DISSOLVING AT POLES."

"SEA WILL RISE 40 FEET."

(Communicated.)

The world is gradually becoming both warmer and drier. One day the great Polar icecaps may melt—raising the level of the oceans from 40 to 50 feet, and wiping half of England from the map.

These suggestions were made by Sir Douglas Mawson (the famous Polar explorer) and Dr. C. E. P. Brooks (of the British Meteorological Office), who is a leading authority on the effect of Polar conditions on climate.

In the same year, a U.S. newspaper, the *Oakland Tribune*, reported that melting polar ice might raise sea levels by up to 150 feet (46 metres) and: 'engulf the world'.

The article was enlivened with an artist's impression of a flooded New York – a similar picture was used for a book cover in 2020:

Perhaps that's a perfect example of recycling? So it must be good for the planet.

CHAPTER 2

The 1960s/1970s Global Cooling scare

THE EARTH STARTS COOLING

In the mid to late 1940s, the Earth started cooling. By the 1970s, there had been so much cooling that scientists were beginning to sound the alarm about what this might mean for the survival of mankind:

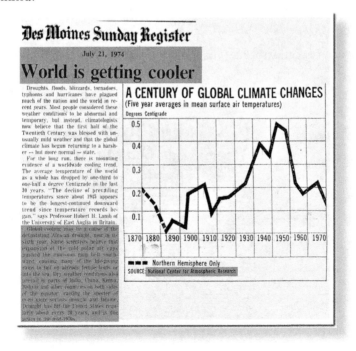

In an interview reported in the above article, one of the world's leading climatologists said: 'For the long run, there is mounting evidence of a worldwide cooling trend. The average temperature for the world as a whole has dropped by one third to one half of a degree Centigrade in the last thirty years. The decline of prevailing temperatures since 1945 appears to be the longest continued downward trend since temperature records began.'

It might be worth mentioning that during this 30-year temperature decline, confirmed by one of the world's most respected climatologists, global atmospheric CO_2 levels rose from around 310 parts per million (ppm) to about 330 ppm. Climate realists might be tempted to wonder how temperatures could fall for 30 years while CO_2 levels were rising if increasing atmospheric CO_2 is really the main driver of global warming.

The Washington Post, which is now an ardent purveyor of the dangers of catastrophic man-made global warming, warned us back in 1971 that: 'U.S. scientist sees New Ice Age coming':

This scientist claimed that 'the world could be as little as 50 or 60 years away from a disastrous new Ice Age'. The scientist explained the main reason for the coming Ice Age: 'the fine dust constantly put into the atmosphere by fossil fuel burning could screen out so much sunlight that the average temperature could drop by six degrees . . . such a temperature decrease could be sufficient to trigger an ice age'. The solution the scientist proposed was strikingly similar to the solution now being proposed to stop global warming: 'it may be simply necessary for men to stop most fossil fuel burning – use of coal, oil, natural gas and automobile gasoline'.

In a scientific article written in 1971 two experts, one of whom later became President Obama's scientific adviser on man-made global warming, blamed the coming assumed crisis mainly on pollution from human activities causing global cooling:

'It seems, however, that a competing effect has dominated the situation since 1940. This is the reduced transparency of the atmosphere to incoming light as a result of urban air pollution (smoke, aerosols), agricultural air pollution (dust), and volcanic ash. This screening phenomenon is said to be responsible for the present world cooling trend . . . A final push in the cooling direction comes from man-made changes in the direct reflectivity of the earth's surface (albedo) through urbanization, deforestation, and the enlargement of deserts.'

The article went on to warn of two possible catastrophes resulting from this largely man-made global cooling: 'The effects of a new ice age on agriculture and the supportability of large human

populations scarcely need elaborating here. Even more dramatic
results are possible, however; for instance, a sudden outward slumping
in the Antarctic ice cap, induced by added weight, could generate a
tidal wave of proportions unprecedented in recorded history.'

In January 1974, the UK's *Guardian* newspaper, also now a
committed believer in and proselytizer of catastrophic
anthropogenic global warming, reported that satellite observations
had confirmed that the Earth was cooling and that a new Ice Age
was on its way:

THE GUARDIAN Tuesday January 29 1974

Space satellites show new Ice. Age coming fast

By ANTHONY TUCKER, Science Correspondent

WORLDWIDE and rapid trends towards a mini Ice Age are emerging from the first long term analyses of satellite weather pictures.

Of potentially great importance to energy strategies and to agriculture, but barely observable yet in Britain because our weather is strongly buffered by the Atlantic, a preliminary analysis carried out at Columbia University, New York, by the European climatologists Doctors George and Helena Kukla indicates that snow and ice cover of the earth increased by 12 per cent during 1967-1972.

This appears to be in keeping with other long-term climatic changes, all of which suggest that after reaching a climax of warmth between 1935 and 1955, world average temperatures are now falling. But the rate of increase of snow and ice cover is much faster than would be expected from other trends.

The technique employed, which was first described in this country last year during a conference at the Climatic Research Unit at the University of East Anglia, depends on the averaging of information from standard and infra-red satellite weather pictures. In spite of the newness of the technique the findings are important and it is a matter of some urgency that they should be re-examined by other groups.

It is particularly important to know whether the earth's reflectivity is changing, for this is one of the factors in which a change tends to be self-perpetuating until some new worldwide balance is reached. An increase of snow and ice cover coupled with a decrease in cloud, or even with no change in cloud cover, means that more of the incoming energy from the sun is reflected straight out again, thus further reducing temperatures.

The Columbia University findings suggest that at present the main changes are not in the general area of winter snow and ice coverage but in the continuation of coverage later and later into the spring. This appears to be true of both the northern and southern hemispheres.

In the highly complex dynamics of world weather patterns an interconnection of some kind between major events is inevitable, but often obscure. It could be, for example, that the extraordinary occurrence of a stationary low pressure area over Brisbane, with its attendant disas-

trous flooding, is a feature of the overall trend.

The Brisbane low pressure area appears to have started life as a normal Pacific cyclonic feature moving along a normal south-easterly curving track. But instead of recurving towards the southwest, it was blocked by an anticyclone to the south of Australia. It happens that blocking anticyclones play an important role in the characteristics of weather in the northern hemisphere and account for some adverse changes in our own climate. The trends appear to be cyclic, fairly long-term and extremely important. It is therefore surprising that, in Britain at least, support for scientific analysis of the history of climate is almost non-existent.

But Nottingham at least is fighting off the advancing ice age — grass is growing and seeds are sprouting there now.

The artificial spring has been created by the underground hot water pipes which now carry heat to thousands of homes in the city. As an experiment city officials scattered grass seeds on wasteland near the central library and grass is shooting up there and in other places where the pipes are.

The *New York Times*, which just like the *Guardian* for the last
thirty to forty years has repeatedly warned us of the perils of
catastrophic man-made global warming and insisted that there is
'scientific consensus' that rising atmospheric CO_2 from human
activities is the main cause of today's catastrophic global warming,

reported back in 1961 that there was 'unanimous agreement' among scientists that the world was getting colder:

The threat of global cooling was also picked up by leading scientific magazines with headlines like: *The Ice Age Cometh.*

And many articles were written about how global cooling would pose a new challenge to the survival of the human race. For example, one article warned: 'the unusually beneficial climate of the past few decades may be degenerating, facing humanity with a new challenge to survival':

Climate Change:
Chilling Possibilities

The unusually beneficial climate of the past few decades may be degenerating, facing humanity with a new challenge to survival

by John H. Douglas

The *National Geographic* also joined in spreading the message about the world cooling in a November 1976 article which quoted the U.S. National Science Board: 'during the last 20 to 30 years, world temperature has fallen, irregularly at first but more sharply over the last decade.'[2]

And just what is going on with the climate? What changes are taking place around us?

"From 1880 to about 1940 the world—particularly the Northern Hemisphere—went through a period of significant warming," I heard from tall, quiet-spoken Dr. J. Murray Mitchell, Jr., of the National Oceanic and Atmospheric Administration (NOAA); he is one of this nation's most respected climatologists (next page). He went on: "But since about 1940, there has been a distinct drop in average global temperature. It's fallen about half a degree Fahrenheit—even more in high latitudes of the Northern Hemisphere."

England's annual growing season shrank by nine or ten days between 1950 and 1966, Hubert Lamb has noted. In the northern tier of the U. S. Midwest, summer frosts again occasionally damage crops.

Sea ice has returned to Iceland's coasts after more than forty years of virtual absence.

> *During the last 20 to 30 years, world temperature has fallen, irregularly at first but more sharply over the last decade.*
> U. S. NATIONAL SCIENCE BOARD, 1974

Glaciers in Alaska and Scandinavia have slowed their recession; some in Switzerland have begun advancing again.

GLOBAL COOLING WILL LEAD TO MORE EXTREME WEATHER

Scientists now predict that global warming will lead to more extreme weather. But in the 1970s, scientists predicted that there would be an increase in extreme weather events – droughts, floods, blizzards, tornadoes, typhoons and hurricanes – caused by global cooling:

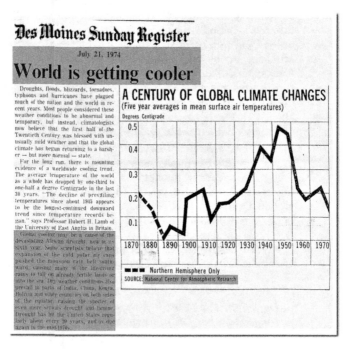

The *Des Moines Sunday Register* reported in 1974:

'Droughts, floods, blizzards, tornadoes, typhoons and hurricanes have plagued much of the nation and the world in recent years. Most people consider these weather conditions to be abnormal and temporary. But instead climatologists now believe that the first half of the Twentieth Century was blessed with unusually mild weather and that the global climate has begun returning to a harsher – but more normal – state. For the long run there is mounting evidence of a worldwide cooling trend.'

As for the supposedly disastrous global warming from 1900 to 1940 when thousands died from a series of heatwaves, this was now referred to as the Earth being: 'blessed with unusually mild weather.'

CROP FAILURES AND STARVATION?

The area of greatest concern for scientists during the 1960s and 1970s global cooling scare seems to have been the likely effect of global cooling and a coming new Ice Age on mankind's food supply.

In 1967, a leading ecologist warned that it was 'already too late' to avoid a disastrous famine by 1975. And he worried about the future of mankind:

'we have to hope that the world famines of the next twenty years will not lead to thermonuclear war and the extinction of the human species.'

The Salt Lake Tribune (Salt Lake City, Utah) · 17 Nov 1957, Fri · Page 5

'Already Too Late'

Dire Famine Forecast by '75

By George Getze
Los Angeles Times Writer

LOS ANGELES — It is already too late for the world to avoid a long period of famine, a Stanford University biologist said Thursday.

Paul Ehrlich said the "time of famines" is upon us and will be at its worst and most disastrous by 1975.

He said the population of the United States is already too big, that birth control may have to be accomplished by making it involuntary and by putting sterilizing agents into staple foods and drinking water, and that the Roman Catholic Church should be pressured into going along with routine measures of population control.

Ehrlich said experts keep saying the world food supply will have to be tripled to feed the six or seven billion people they expect to be living in the year 2000.

"That may be possible theoretically but it is clear that it is totally impossible in practice," he said.

Ehrlich spoke at a science symposium at the University of Texas. The text of his speech was made available here.

Since, in Ehrlich's opinion, it is of no longer any use trying to avoid the coming world famines, the best thing to do now is to look past the "time of famines" and hope to have a second chance to control world population sometime in the future.

"At the moment it is shockingly apparent that the battle to feed humanity will end in a rout," Ehrlich said.

He said we have to hope that the world famines of the next 20 years will not lead to thermonuclear war and the extinction of the human species.

"We must assume man will get another chance, no matter how little he deserves one," he said.

About 40 years later, we would be told by the next generation of experts that global warming would lead to nuclear conflict.[3] So, it seems that whatever the climate does, whether it warms or cools, it will be responsible for the next nuclear war.

In 1970, the same gentleman predicted: 'America will be subject to water rationing by 1974 and food rationing by 1980.'

In August 1974, the *New York Times* announced that 'Climate Changes Endanger World's Food Output' and warned that due to global cooling 'mankind is on the threshold of a new pattern of adverse global climate for which it is ill-prepared':

A leading climate scientist, Professor Hubert H. Lamb, from the University of East Anglia in Britain was quoted as suggesting that global cooling could be harmful for the world's food production: 'global cooling may be a cause of the devastating African drought now in its sixth year. Some scientists believe that expansion of the cold polar ice caps pushed the monsoon rain belt southward causing many of the life-giving rains to fall on already fertile lands or into the sea.'

It was Professor Lamb who in 1971 founded the Climatic Research Unit at the University of East Anglia. The Climatic Research Unit has since become one of the most vociferous proponents of the theory of CO2-driven CAGW and was the source of the leaked emails in the 2009 Climategate scandal when critics accused the Climatic Research Unit of doctoring temperature records and conspiring to suppress any scientists who expressed any doubts about the theory that global warming was mainly caused by increasing amounts of CO2 in the atmosphere from human activities.

Similarly, the *Associated Press* reported in 1974 that the U.S. National Centre for Atmospheric Research predicted 'a period of unstable climate, crop losses, food shortages and death by starvation for millions' because 'the world is moving into a period of cooler temperatures.'

GREELEY (Colo.) TRIBUNE   Wed., June 12, 1974

Boulder scientists see end of period of favorable weather

SCIENTISTS—Dr. Stephen H. Schneider, left, and Dr. Walter Orr Roberts, both of the National Center for Atmospheric Research, give way to an unstable climate leading to crop losses, food shortages and death by starvation say their research on global weather indicates for millions. (AP Wirephoto)

By BILL JORDAN
Boulder Camera
(Written for Associated Press)

BOULDER, Colo. (AP) —Observers of the global climate at the National Center for Atmospheric Research believe the favorable weather of the past 15 years is about to give way to a period of unstable climate, crop losses, food shortages and death by starvation for millions.

Underlying Schneider's ideas on food shortages is the knowledge that the world is moving into a period of cooler temperatures.

SCIENTISTS WARN THE U.S. PRESIDENT

On 26th and 27th January 1972, a group of leading climate scientists held a conference at the Department of Geological Science at Brown University on Rhode Island. The conference 'dealt with the past and future changes of climate and was attended by 42 top American and European investigators.'

The attendees were so concerned about the likely effects of global cooling that they wrote a letter to the then President Richard Nixon. In the letter, the scientists warned of:

1. Substantially lowered food production due to the shorter growing seasons and changed rain distribution in the main producing belts of the world, with Eastern Europe and Central Asia to be first affected

2. Increased frequency and amplitude of extreme weather anomalies such as those bringing floods, snowstorms, killing frosts etc

Following the letter to the President from Brown University, various U.S. government departments including the Defense Advanced Research Projects Agency and the Interdepartmental Committee on Atmospheric Sciences (ICAS) were tasked with investigating the likely results of global cooling. One of ICAS's aims was:

'Identification and description of adverse climatic effects, such as sustained extreme weather anomalies, changed rain distribution, and shortened growing seasons which would be likely to occur.'

THE CIA PREDICTS RISING POLITICAL INSTABILITY

In 1976, the U.S. Central Intelligence Agency (CIA) issued a discussion paper titled *Potential Implications of Trends in World Population, Food Production, and Climate*. In the discussion paper's introduction, the CIA authors stated that:

'there is, moreover, growing consensus among leading climatologists that the world is undergoing a cooling trend':

OPR-401
August 1974

Potential Implications of Trends in World Population, Food Production, and Climate

THE DISCUSSION

I. INTRODUCTION

The widespread crop shortfalls in 1972 and the energy and fertilizer crunches in '73 and '74 have raised anew the basic question of whether the production of food can keep pace with demand over the next few decades. Concern about the capability of many of the poorer countries to provide for their growing population is widespread and rising. Major international conferences planned for the second half of this year--i.e., the World Population Conference in August and the World Food Conference in November-- will focus on various aspects of this question.

There is, moreover, growing consensus among leading climatologists that the world is undergoing a cooling trend. If it continues, as feared, it could restrict production in both the USSR and China among other states, and could have an enormous impact, not only on the food-population balance, but also on the world balance of power.

CIA experts worried that 'major climatic changes will bring about global unrest of a proportion almost beyond comprehension, heightening the risk of international conflict':

PAGE 6 - DAILY NEWS - MAY 4, 1976

Climatic Changes Would Bring Global Unrest, CIA Report Says

WASHINGTON, May 3, Reuter - Major climatic changes will bring about global unrest of a proportion almost beyond comprehension, heightening the risk of international conflict, according to a Central Intelligence Agency (CIA) report released today.

The report said world climate changes would sharply reduce crop production and spread drought, famine and political unrest throughout the world.

The adverse weather is likely to last for at least 40 years and possibly for centuries, the report said.

The report was based on a working paper prepared by the CIA's Office of Research and Development from a study by Dr. Reid A. Bryson of the University of Wisconsin, an expert on climatology.

The report said the climate change began in 1960 but no one recognized it.

It said the crop failures in the Soviet Union and India during the first part of the 1960s were attributed to the natural fluctuation of the weather.

The report said the adverse climate, according to the University of Wisconsin study, would mean that India will suffer a major drought every four years, resulting in the starvation of 150 million people.

China will suffer a major famine every five years and the Soviet Union will lose its wheat fields in Kazakhstan, the report said.

The Soviet Union will thus show an yearly loss of 48 million metric tons of grain and China would require a supply of 50 million metric tons of grain to feed its population.

Canada, a major exporter, would lose over 50 per cent in production capability and 75 per cent of its exporting capabilities.

Northern Europe would lose 25 to 30 per cent of its present production capability while the Common Market "would zero their exports," the report added.

Warning of a major shift in the earth's climate already underway, the report said: "The economic and political impact of a major climatic shift is almost beyond comprehension.

"Any nation with scientific knowledge of the atmospheric sciences will challenge this natural climatic change," it declared. "The potential for international conflict due to controlled climate modification can be a reality in the 1970s."

The report was prepared in August, 1974. The CIA said its views and conclusions did not necessarily represent the agency's official position.

A copy of the report containing some deletions was released by Congressman Fred Richmond (Demo, New York)

Mr. Richmond also released segments of another CIA report prepared in August, 1974, which said grave food shortages would tempt powerful but hungry countries to obtain grain by any means they could.

Massive migrations from one country to another, sometimes backed by force, would be a live issue and consequently political and economic instability would be widespread, the report said.

The CIA stated that: 'the stability of most nations is based upon a dependable source of food, but this stability will not be possible under the new climate era.' The CIA report predicted that: 'the politics of food will become the central issue of every government' and 'grave food shortages would tempt powerful but hungry countries to obtain grain by any means they could.' The CIA also foresaw that: 'massive migrations from one country to another, sometimes backed by force would be a live issue and consequently political and economic instability would be widespread.'

These are, of course, very similar to the claims being made by today's climate catastrophists about global warming:

'Rich areas like the U.S. and Europe would become "virtual fortresses" to prevent millions of migrants from entering, after being forced from land drowned by sea-level rise or no longer able to grow crops.'[4]

On 1st August 1974, the U.S. Government asked the Commerce Department to set up a new subcommittee to assess the effects of climate change (global cooling).

In spite of the CIA's reports and the activities of the Commerce Department's subcommittee on Climate Change, in 1975 Newsweek reported that scientists were pessimistic that political leaders around the world would act to mitigate the impending dangers caused by global cooling:

'Climatologists are pessimistic that political leaders will take any positive action to compensate for the climatic change or even to allay its effects ... Scientists see few signs that government leaders anywhere are even prepared to take of stockpiling food.'

The *Newsweek* article ended with the type of apocalyptic warning that we should have become used to from today's catastrophic anthropogenic global warming alarmists:

'The longer the planners delay, the more difficult will they find it to cope with climatic change once the results become grim reality.'[5]

HOW TO HEAT UP THE COOLING EARTH

As scientists feared the effects of the Earth's cooling, they proposed a number of ambitious geoengineering projects to try to slow down or even reverse the cooling trend. One of these was to try to get the Arctic ice cap to melt by covering it with black soot:

SCIENCE

The Cooling World

Climatologists are pessimistic that political leaders will take any positive action to compensate for the climatic change, or even to allay its effects. They concede that some of the more spectacular solutions proposed, such as melting the arctic ice cap by covering it with black soot or diverting arctic rivers, might create problems far greater than those they solve. But the scientists see few signs that government leaders anywhere are even prepared to take the simple measures of stockpiling food or of introducing the variables of climatic uncertainty into economic projections of future food supplies. The longer the planners delay, the more difficult will they find it to cope with climatic change once the results become grim reality.

—PETER GWYNNE with bureau reports

Newsweek, April 28, 1975

This idea for reversing global cooling was also reported in the *New York Times*:[6]

Among the hypotheses to be assessed is one that attributes ice ages to the absence of pack ice on the Arctic Ocean. Winds off that ocean are very dry and drop little snow on Northern lands, but if the sea were open the snows would be heavy and ice sheets would begin to form, the hypothesis holds.

Such an idea assumes that the ocean, once free of ice, would not soon freeze again. At present, the brilliant snow surface of the pack reflects much solar energy back into space. If the ocean were ice-free, it is argued, this would not occur, and the water would warm up enough to prevent refreezing.

Other Proposals

Other scientists have proposed that, by sprinkling coal dust on the pack, or through other manipulation, it would be possible to melt the ice, open the ocean to navigation and ameliorate the northern climate.

This is the same *New York Times*, which 50 years later (February 2021), suggested we fill the atmosphere with chemicals to dim the sun to reverse global warming:

The New York Times

Feb. 9, 2021

Should We Dim the Sun? Will We Even Have a Choice?

Elizabeth Kolbert and Ezra Klein discuss what options remain if our political system can't handle the climate crisis.

Another idea to stop global cooling and warm up the Earth was to melt the Arctic Ice Cap by building a dam across the Bering

Strait and pumping the cold Arctic Ocean waters into the warmer
Pacific Ocean:

As science learns more about the
weather and climate, more schemes to
control them are suggested. Weather
modification has come a long way from
early cloud-seeding experiments, and
now is considered an operational technology capable of snow suppression or
augmentation, hail reduction, fog dis-
sipation, lightning alteration and hurricane modification. The Pentagon has admitted conducting a seven-year weather
warfare program in Indochina, and a
U.S.-Soviet meeting is planned this year
to consider limits on such activity.

Meanwhile, Soviet scientists have dis-
cussed damming the Bering Strait and
pumping Arctic Ocean waters into the
Pacific, or diverting the great Siberian
rivers southward. Both projects would
partly melt the polar ice caps and raise
global temperatures — along with the
level of the world's oceans.

Given that predicted food shortages would be caused by global
cooling crop failures, one leading
ecologist even proposed putting
sterility drugs into food in order
to slow down the increase in the
world's human population:

The New York Times

TUESDAY, NOVEMBER 25, 1969

A STERILITY DRUG IN FOOD IS HINTED

Biologist Stresses Need to Curb Population Growth

By GLADWIN HILL
Special to The New York Times

SAN FRANCISCO, Nov. 24
—A possibility that the Government might have to put sterility
drugs in reservoirs and in food
shipped to foreign countries to
limit human multiplication was
envisioned today by a leading
crusader on the population
problem.

The crusader, Dr. Paul Ehrlich of Stanford University,
among a number of commenta-
tors who called attention to the
"population crisis" as the United States Commission for Unesco opened it 13th national conference here today.

Unesco is the United Nations
Educational, Scientific and Cultural Organization. The 100-
member commission, appointed
by the Secretary of State, included representatives of Government, outside organizations
and the public. Some 500 con-
servationists and others are at-
tending the two-day meeting at
the St. Francis Hotel, devoted
this year to environmental
problems.

WILL THE COOLING EVER END?

By 1978, scientists feared that the global cooling, which had started in the 1940s, would never end:

The New York Times

International Team of Specialists Finds No End in Sight to 30-Year Cooling Trend in Northern Hemisphere

By WALTER SULLIVAN   JAN. 5, 1978

Fortunately the 'international team of specialists' quoted by the *New York Times* didn't have to wait too long. Within just a few years, the Earth had started warming again. So there was no need to cover the Arctic ice with black soot; no need to melt the Arctic Ice Cap by building a dam across the Bering Strait and pumping the cold Arctic Ocean waters into the warmer Pacific Ocean; and no need to lace our food with sterility drugs to stop us reproducing.

PART 2

The Alarmists' apocalyptic warnings

'In individuals, insanity is rare; but in groups, parties, nations and epochs, it is the rule.'

– Friedrich Nietzsche

CHAPTER 3

Melting ice?

The man-made global warming alarmists generally focus on four main subjects when warning us of the catastrophic effects of human activities on the world's ice:

1. The Arctic ice cap melting
2. Greenland's ice cover melting
3. Antarctic ice melting
4. The threat of less ice to animals like polar bears and walruses

STUBBORN ARCTIC ICE DEFIES GLOOMSTERS'
PREDICTIONS

We were warned and warned and warned

Anyone looking for climate alarmist predictions of the Arctic sea ice melting in the summer would be spoilt for choice. In 2007, the formerly respected *National Geographic* suggested that: 'Arctic sea ice gone in summer within five years?':

NATIONAL GEOGRAPHIC NEWS
REPORTING YOUR WORLD DAILY

Arctic Sea Ice Gone in Summer Within Five Years?

Seth Borenstein in Washington
Associated Press
December 12, 2007

An already relentless melting of the Arctic greatly accelerated this summer—a sign that some scientists worry could mean global warming has passed an ominous tipping point.

The *National Geographic* wrote that:

'An already relentless meting of the Arctic greatly accelerated this summer – a sign that some scientists worry could mean global warming has passed an ominous tipping point.'

The following year, 2008, the *National Geographic* upped the ante when it brought forward the day of disaster by four years when it claimed: 'North Pole May Be Ice-Free For First Time This Summer':

North Pole May Be Ice-Free for First Time This Summer

Aalok Mehta aboard the C.C.G.S. *Amundsen*
National Geographic News
June 20, 2008

Arctic warming has become so dramatic that the North Pole may melt this summer, report scientists studying the effects of climate change in the field.

"We're actually projecting this year that the North Pole may be free of ice for the first time [in history]," David Barber, of the University of Manitoba, told National Geographic News aboard the C.C.G.S. *Amundsen*, a Canadian research icebreaker.

When that didn't happen, scientists wondered: 'Could all Arctic ice be gone by 2012?'

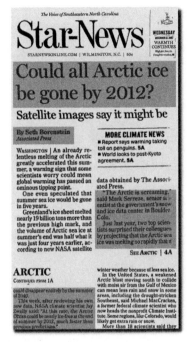

And we were told that: 'The Arctic is screaming.'

In 2007, the BBC (British Broadcasting Corporation) warned us that: 'Arctic summers ice-free by 2013.' The BBC explained:

'Scientists in the U.S. have presented one of the most dramatic forecasts yet for the disappearance of Arctic sea ice. Their latest modelling studies indicate northern polar waters could be ice-free in summers within just 5-6 years.'

This prediction was echoed by other experts:

In a Sierra Club Canada article in March 2013 one scientist wrote:

> 'For the record I do not think that any sea ice will survive
> this summer.'

Four years earlier, in 2009, Al Gore had predicted: 'Polar ice cap
may disappear by summer 2014' because 'new computer modelling
suggests the Arctic Ocean may be nearly ice-free in summer as
early as 2014, Al Gore said today at the U.N. Climate conference
in Copenhagen':

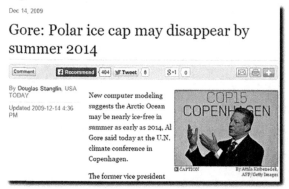

In 2013, the UK *Guardian* newspaper predicted a 'methane catastrophe' due to an ice-free Arctic by 2015:

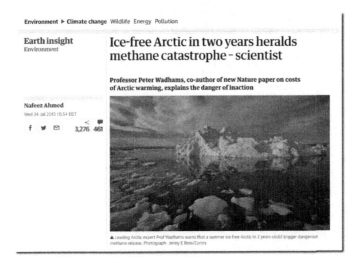

A little later that year, in December 2013, the *Guardian* moved the date of its Arctic ice catastrophe out by another year to 2016:

theguardian
US Navy predicts summer ice free Arctic by 2016

Is conventional modelling out of pace with speed and abruptness of global warming?

In 2016, there was still summer sea ice in the Arctic. But the *Guardian* wasn't going to let itself be discouraged by anything as unreliable as reality. In August 2016, the *Guardian* predicted that the Arctic would be free of ice in 2017 or 2018:

theguardian
'Next year or the year after, the Arctic will be free of ice'
Robin McKie

Sunday 21 August 2016 02.00 EDT

When none of these forecasts of an ice-free Arctic actually materialised, in August 2020 the *National Geographic*, which had previously assured us that 2008 was the year of the Arctic sea ice disaster, pushed out the date of this calamity a bit further when the magazine claimed: 'Arctic summer ice could disappear as early as 2035:'

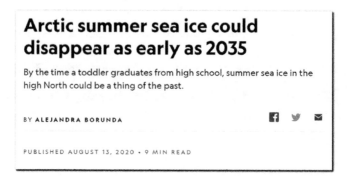

Arctic summer sea ice could disappear as early as 2035

By the time a toddler graduates from high school, summer sea ice in the high North could be a thing of the past.

BY ALEJANDRA BORUNDA

PUBLISHED AUGUST 13, 2020 · 9 MIN READ

Meanwhile back at the *Guardian*, it might seem as if *Guardian* journalists were getting a bit fed up with obstinate Arctic sea ice which frustratingly wouldn't melt as the *Guardian* kept predicting. So the *Guardian* moved on to Greenland and warned us that the Greenland ice sheet would face a 'tipping point' by 2020. The *Guardian* predicted:

'The entire ice mass of Greenland will disappear from the world map if temperatures rise by as little as 2°C, with severe consequences for the rest of the world . . . The fall-out would be felt thousands of miles away from the Arctic, unleashing a global sea level rise of 23 feet (7 metres).'[7]

EXPEDITIONS TO REALITY?

A problem with many of the predictions of a summer ice-free Arctic is that the computer models were based on the assumption that increasing CO_2 in the atmosphere, caused mainly by humans burning fossil fuels, would automatically lead to increasing temperatures and thus a melting Arctic. But when intrepid climate warriors set off on real expeditions in the real world to prove that the computer models were correct, the results were not always in line with their predictions.

For example, expecting a fairly ice-free Arctic in 2008, an adventurer aimed to kayak 1,200 km (745 miles) from Norway across the ice-free Arctic all the way to the North Pole. According to a BBC report, the journey was expected to take between two and three weeks. The adventurer was followed by a support ship, no doubt powered by the kind of fossil fuel that global warming extinctionists so detest:

BBC | Sign In   News   Sport   Weather   Capital

NEWS   ▶ Watch ONE-MINUTE WORLD NEWS

Page last updated at 00:06 GMT, Saturday, 30 August 2008 01:06 UK

Swimmer aims to kayak to N Pole

This year, for the first time, scientists predict that the North Pole could briefly be ice free and that has inspired Mr Pugh to try to find a way through.

On Saturday he is due to set off on the 1200km (745 mile) expedition from Norway to the North Pole - a journey expected to take between two and three weeks. A support ship will follow the kayak to provide Mr Pugh with food and respite from the brutal conditions.

"This will be my hardest challenge to date," the self-proclaimed "Ice Bear" told me.

Lewis Pugh did part of his training in the icy waters off northern Norway

The aim of the expedition was to highlight the melting sea ice. Unfortunately there was so much ice blocking the way that the 1,200 km expedition had to be abandoned just 135 km from the start.

In his biography, the adventurer blamed global warming for his expedition's failure:

'Ironically, global warming played no small part in undermining the entire expedition. We believed that the greater melting of summer ice would open up large areas of sea and allow us to paddle north at good speed. What we did not fully appreciate was that to the north of us there was a widespread melting of sea ice off the coast of Alaska and the New Siberian Islands and the ice was being pushed south towards us'.[8]

Someone of a more unkind or even cynical disposition might be tempted to conclude that the reason the trip only managed 135 km of the planned 1,200 km was that there was too much Arctic sea ice.

In 2011, another group headed off into the Arctic again to draw the world's attention to how man-made global warming was harming the Arctic ice cap. An expedition member reported that:

'Throughout the first week or so temperatures rarely rose above -40°C, -60°C with wind-chill. Nothing worked in those sorts of temperatures; your kit doesn't work, you don't work, and it's all just horrendous. The sleek expensive radar we had brought along that was supposed to measure the thickness of the ice as we were walking didn't turn on at all in those temperatures, even though we tested it thoroughly in − 50 °C fridges before we left. Martin's video camera wouldn't operate for the first two weeks. Instead he had to take all his video footage using my little Panasonic Lumix pocket camera, tucked deep in the folds of his clothing to protect it against the elements. He shot everything on that little camera to begin with, even footage for the 'News at Ten', such was the fallibility of our technology to the omnipresent cold'.

At the end of the expedition, after 74 days trekking across the ice taking various measurements of things like ice thickness and pressure ridges, the team had to wait for 12 days huddled in their sleeping bags in their tents, surviving mainly on chocolate and nuts, because the weather was so bad that the plane which was due to pick them up couldn't land.

IS THE ARCTIC SEA ICE REALLY MELTING?

The amount of sea ice in the Arctic has varied considerably since measurements began in 1925 (Figure 1).

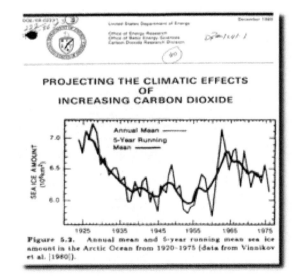

Figure 1 – Arctic sea ice amount 1925 to 1975

As would be expected, in the warming years which started in the 1880s and ended in the 1940s, there was a decline in the amount of sea ice from over 7 million square kilometres (km²) to just above 6 million km². Then in the 'Little Cooling', which followed the 1950s, the amount of sea ice started to stabilise and then rise, briefly peaking above 7 million km² again before dropping down towards 6 million km².

If the Arctic sea ice were to melt, it's thought that without ice to reflect back the sun's rays, the water would absorb more heat which would lead to accelerating global warming. In its 1,526-page U.S. National Climate Assessment fourth report written in 2017/18 and published in 2018, the U.S. Global Change Research Programme presented a diagram showing what the report calls 'Climate Change Indicators'. One of these Climate Change Indicators was a chart of Arctic sea-ice levels falling since 1979. That's the chart on the lower line of the diagram – the chart that is highlighted with shading:

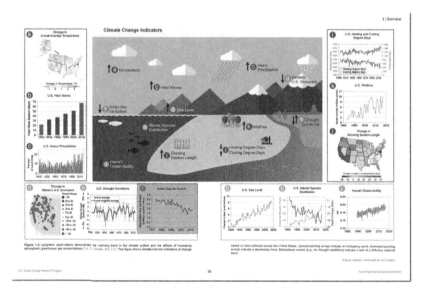

Figure 2 below shows the Arctic sea-ice chart from the U.S. National Climate Assessment report in close-up. The fairly precipitous drop in the amount of Arctic sea ice after 1979 seems to confirm the global warming alarmists' claims of impending catastrophe from melting Arctic sea ice.

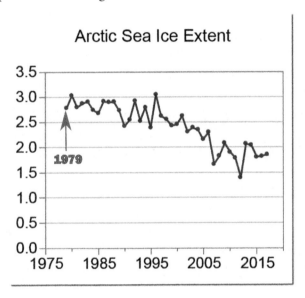

Figure 2 – Arctic sea-ice extent 1979 to 2017

The reason for starting the graph in 1979 is supposedly because that was the year when satellites first started measuring Arctic sea-ice coverage. The two smoking guns which demolish the climate alarmists' claims of sea ice collapsing to historically record low levels can be found in two places. Firstly, there is the 1990 report from the IPCC (Intergovernmental Panel on Climate Change) using data supplied by NOAA (the U.S. National Oceanic and Atmospheric Administration). The text in the IPCC report shows that satellite measurements began at the start of the 1970s and not in 1979:

'satellite observations have been used to map sea-ice extent routinely since the early 1970s. The American Navy Joint Ice Center has produced weekly charts which have been digitised by NOAA':

Sea-ice conditions are now reported regularly in marine synoptic observations, as well as by special reconnaissance flights, and coastal radar. Especially importantly, satellite observations have been used to map sea-ice extent routinely since the early 1970s. The American Navy Joint Ice Center has produced weekly charts which have been digitised by NOAA. These data are summarized in Figure 7.20 which is based on analyses carried out on a 1° latitude x 2.5° longitude grid. Sea-ice is defined to be present when its concentration exceeds 10% (Ropelewski, 1983). Since about 1976 the areal extent of sea-ice in the Northern Hemisphere has varied about a constant climatological level but in 1972-1975 sea-ice extent was significantly less.

The second smoking gun appears in a *Guardian* newspaper report from 1974, which I have already used in Chapter 2. The headline: 'Space satellites show new ice age coming fast' makes it clear that satellites were already in full use in 1974 and probably slightly before that.

THE GUARDIAN Tuesday January 29 1974

Space satellites show new Ice.Age coming fast

By ANTHONY TUCKER, Science Correspondent

WORLDWIDE and rapid trends towards a mini Ice Age are emerging from the first long term analyses of satellite weather pictures.

Of potentially great importance to energy strategies and to agriculture, but barely observable yet in Britain because our weather is strongly buffered by the Atlantic, a preliminary analysis carried out at Columbia University, New York, by the European climatologists Doctors George and Helena Kukla indicates that snow and ice cover of the earth increased by 12 per cent during 1967-1972.

This appears to be in keeping with other long-term climatic changes, all of which suggest that after reaching a climax of warmth between 1935 and 1955, world average temperatures are now falling. But the rate of increase of snow and ice cover is much faster than would be expected from other trends.

The technique employed, which was first described in this country last year during a conference at the Climatic Research Unit at the University of East Anglia, depends on the averaging of information from standard and infra - red satellite weather pictures. In spite of the newness of the technique the findings are important and it is a matter of some urgency that they should be re-examined by other groups.

It is particularly important to know whether the earth's reflectivity is changing, for this is one of the factors in which a change tends to be self-perpetuating until some new worldwide balance is reached. An increase of snow and ice cover coupled with a decrease in cloud, or even with no change in cloud cover, means that more of the incoming energy from the sun is reflected straight out again, thus further reducing temperatures.

The Columbia University findings suggest that at present the main changes are not in the general area of winter snow and ice coverage but in the continuation of coverage later and later into the spring. This appears to be true of both the northern and southern hemispheres.

In the highly complex dynamics of world weather patterns an interconnection of some kind between major events is inevitable, but often obscure. It could be, for example, that the extraordinary occurrence of a stationary low pressure area over Brisbane, with its attendant disas-trous flooding, is a feature of the overall trend.

The Brisbane low pressure area appears to have started life as a normal Pacific cyclonic feature moving along a normal south-easterly curving track. But instead of recurving towards the south-west, it was blocked by an anticyclone to the south of Australia. It happens that blocking anticyclones play an important role in the characteristics of weather in the northern hemisphere and account for some adverse changes in our own climate. The trends appear to be cyclic, fairly long-term and extremely important. It is therefore surprising that, in Britain at least, support for scientific analysis of the history of climate is almost non-existent.

But Nottingham at least is fighting off the advancing ice age — grass is growing and seeds are sprouting there now.

The artificial spring has been created by the underground hot water pipes which now carry heat to thousands of homes in the city. As an experiment city officials scattered grass seeds on wasteland near the central library and grass is shooting up from and in other areas where the pipes are.

Moreover, the *Guardian* article proved that Arctic sea ice was increasing around 1974, hence the *Guardian*'s 1974 prediction of a new Ice Age.

So, the chart in the National Climate Assessment report (Figure 2) showing sea ice extent declining after 1979 could be accused of being more than misleading. If we look at the Arctic sea ice chart from the IPCC report (Figure 3), we can see that NOAA had started measuring Arctic sea ice as early as 1972/3. We can also see that Arctic sea ice was lower than average between 1972 and 1975. This is confirmed by the IPCC report: 'in 1972-1975 sea-ice extent was significantly less.' Arctic sea ice then increased reaching a peak in 1979. By 'forgetting' the 1972 to 1975 low sea-ice levels and starting their charts at the 1979 record high Arctic sea ice, the

National Climate Assessment can create the impression that sea-ice levels are diminishing rapidly (Figure 3). In Figure 3, the rising levels of Arctic sea ice from 1973 to the peak in 1979, which were cut from the National Climate Assessment chart, have been shaded.

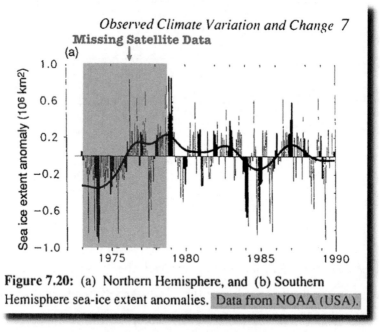

Figure 3 – The sea-ice chart in the IPCC report shows that ice reached a record high level in 1979

In fact, we know from newspaper reports at the time that there was a significant increase in Arctic sea ice in the decade from 1965 to 1975. On 2 March 1975, the *Chicago Tribune* newspaper reported:

'In the last decade the Arctic ice and snow cap has expanded 12 per cent, and for the first time in this century, ships making for Iceland ports have been impeded by drifting ice.'

Arctic sea ice continued increasing from 1975 to 1979. Moreover, we can see confirmation that Arctic sea ice would be high in 1979, as 1979 was the coldest year on record since 1900, by looking at the NASA (National Aeronautics and Space Administration) data for the surface temperature in Reykjavik for the last 120 years (Figure 4).

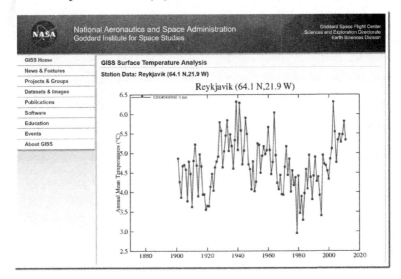

Figure 4 – NASA temperatures show 1979 was a record cold year in the polar region

Given that Arctic sea ice seems to have reached a record high by the record cold year of 1979, it's not surprising (nor is it a matter for panicked concern) if the level of Arctic sea ice has fallen since the 1979 record high. Figure 5 shows how climate alarmists seem to have deliberately used the coldest year to start the ice-level chart they supplied to the U.S. National Climate Assessment in order to create the impression of disastrous warming and ice melting when, in reality, the amount of Arctic sea ice was just declining back to a more normal level from the record 1979 high.

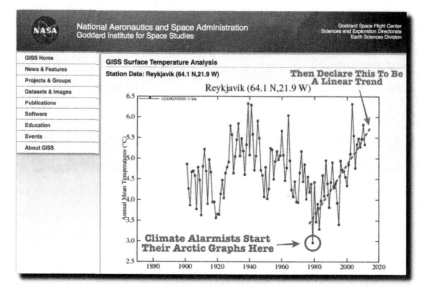

Figure 5 – How alarmists have chosen their chart's starting point

The U.S. National Snow and Ice Data Center also start their Arctic ice-level charts in the record cold year of 1979 (Figure 6).

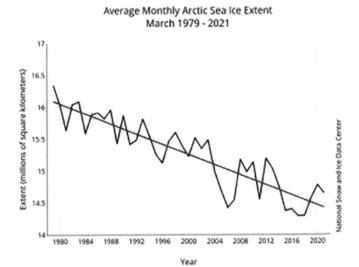

Figure 6 – National Snow and Ice Data Center
Arctic Sea Ice Extent 1979 to 2021

It should be clear that by being presented a partial picture of Arctic sea-ice levels, we are being hoodwinked into believing the CAGW narrative when the facts tell a quite different story.

Moreover, in direct contradiction to the climate change catastrophists' 'shocking' warnings about allegedly rapidly-melting Arctic sea ice, the two main measures of Arctic sea-ice extent – MASIE (Multisensor Analysed Sea Ice Extent) and the DMI (Danish Meteorological Institute) show a very limited decline in Arctic sea ice in the last few years. Here's the MASIE Arctic sea-ice extent during each year from 2006 to 2020 (Figure 7).

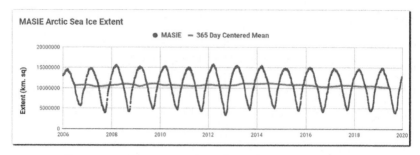

Figure 7 – Arctic sea ice throughout the year (2006 to 2020)

And here's the DMI chart from 2016 to April 2021 (Figure 8).

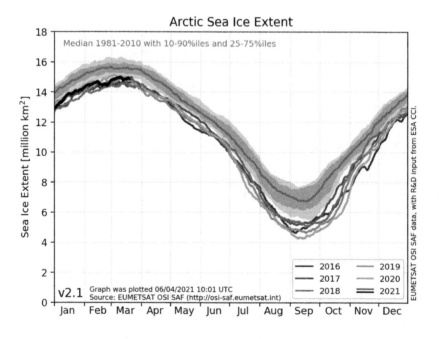

Figure 8 – Arctic sea ice extent throughout each year (2016 to 2021)

The 2021 level is the thick black line which ends at April. The upper line with the shaded area around it represents the median ice level from 1981 to 2010. You'll see that all the years from 2016 to 2020 are significantly below the median for 1981 to 2010. But January to April 2021 is slightly above the years 2016 to 2020. So there has predictably been some melting during the global warming that has occurred since the Little Cooling that ended around the start of the 1980s. But you'll also see that the level of ice has not changed at all in the five years since 2016 in spite of the hyperbolic claims of impending catastrophe from over-excited, reality-denying climate alarmists and tame global-warming-propagandising journalists.

THE ARCTIC HAS BEEN A LOT WARMER THAN IT IS TODAY

Climate alarmists frequently claim that the Arctic ice melt that started in 1979 is 'unprecedented'. However there is a lot of evidence that there was a similar Arctic sea-ice melt during the warm period from the 1880s to the start of the 1940s. In November 1922, a newspaper article quoted a report that the American consul in Bergen, Norway, made to the State Department in Washington D.C. that: 'The Arctic Ocean is warming up, icebergs are growing scarce and in some places the seals are finding the waters too hot.' The newspaper article went on to claim: 'Reports from fishermen, seal hunters and explorers all point to a radical change in climatic conditions and hitherto unheard of temperatures in the Arctic zone.'

The BARTON COUNTY DEMOCRAT

THE GREAT BEND TRIBUNE
THURSDAY, NOVEMBER 2, 1922

ARCTIC OCEAN WARMING UP.

In Some Places Seals Are Finding Waters Too Hot, Says Report.

WASHINGTON, Nov. 2.—The Arctic ocean is warming up, icebergs are growing scarce and in some places the seals are finding the waters too hot, according to a report to the commerce department today from Consul Ifft, at Bergen Norway.

Reports from fishermen, seal hunters and explorers, he declared, all point to a radical change in climatic conditions and hitherto unheard of temperatures in the Artic zone, exploration expeditions reporting that scarcely any ice has been met with as far north as 81 degrees 29 minutes.

Great masses of ice have been replaced by moraines of earth and stones, the report continued while at many points well known glaciers have entirely disappeared. Very few seals and no white fish are being found in the eastern Arctic, while vast shoals of herring and smelts, which have never before ventured so far north, are being encountered in the old seal fishing grounds.

Also in the consul's 1922 report was a claim of a record rise in the temperature of the Arctic Ocean: 'Formerly the waters around Spitzbergen held an even summer temperature of about 3° Celsius; this year recorded temperatures up to 15°, and last winter the ocean did not freeze over even on the north coast of Spitzbergen.'

So serious was the situation, that by 1934 scientists were speculating that melting ice could cause a global flooding disaster possibly raising water levels by up to 150 feet (46 metres):

By 1939, it was reported that the Arctic was warming one degree every two years and that in the 29 years since Arctic temperatures first started being measured in 1910, the winter temperature in the Arctic had warmed by almost 16 degrees:

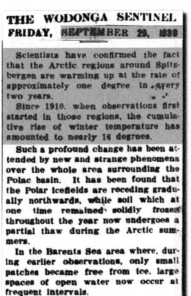

By 1940, high Polar temperatures were still being recorded: 'Polar temperatures are on an average six degrees higher than those registered by Nansen 40 years ago. Ice measurements were on an average only 6½ feet.'

THE TOWNSVILLE DAILY BULLETIN, FRIDAY, FEBRUARY 23, 1940.

THE NORTH POLE.

Is it Getting Warmer.

(From a Special Correspondent. By Air Mail.)

BUNDABERG, February 22.

Is it getting warmer at the North Pole? From soundings and meteorological tests taken by the Soviet explorers who returned this week to Murmansk, Russia's sole ice-free Arctic port, it was concluded that near Polar temperatures are on an average six degrees higher than those registered by Nansen 40 years ago. Ice measurements were on an average only 6½ feet against from 9½ to 13 feet.

At 6½ feet (2 metres), this put the 1940 Arctic sea ice at about the same thickness as it is in 2021.

In 1952, a newspaper reported that: 'The glaciers of Norway and Alaska are only half the size they were 50 years ago. The temperature around Spitzbergen has so modified that the sailing time has lengthened from three to eight months of the year.'[9]

March is usually the month when the Arctic sea ice is thickest. In March 1955, a newspaper reported that the area of Arctic sea ice had halved: 'There are now six million square miles of ice in the Arctic. There were once 12 million square miles.'

And in 1958, the *New York Times* predicted that, within the lifetime of its readers' children, ships would be able to sail over the North Pole:

Democrat and Chronicle
Rochester, N. Y.,
Thurs., Mar. 10, 1955   3

Melting Arctic Ice Warming Up World

By FRANK THOMPSON

BOSTON, March 9 (INS)—A famed Arctic explorer reported today the world is getting warmer—but that's not an unmixed blessing.

Adm. Donald MacMillan, an 80-year-old veteran of 30 trips to the Arctic, said that huge areas of ice in the Far North are melting, bringing warmer weather. But he added that the process also may bring a flooding threat to some parts of Eastern seaboard cities.

MacMillan explained in an interview:

"There are now six million square miles of ice in the Arctic. There once were 12 million square miles.

"Another thing, almost every glacier, with one exception, has retreated—going back into the hills—is smaller than it was.

The New York Times

SUNDAY, OCTOBER 19, 1958

The Changing Face of the Arctic

Some scientists estimate that the polar ice pack is 40 per cent thinner and 12 per cent less in area than it was a half-century ago, and that even within the lifetime of our children the Arctic Ocean may open, enabling ships to sail over the North Pole, as the submarines Nautilus and Skate recently sailed under it. A ship bound from New York to Tokyo would save 2,500

Although the idea that a solid ice sheet covers the central Arctic has lingered stubbornly in the popular fancy, the northern cap of ice worn by our planet is actually a thin crust—on the whole, only about seven feet thick—over an ocean two miles deep in places.

That 1958 prediction of a summer ice-free Arctic in the lifetime of readers' children wasn't terribly dissimilar from the *National Geographic* 2020 prediction (62 years later) that:

> 'By the time a toddler graduates from high school, summer sea ice in the North could be a thing of the past.'

In March 2021, the U.S. National Snow and Ice Data Center reported that the Arctic sea ice was around 14 million km² – around 5½ million square miles (mi²). So the 2021 sea ice coverage was slightly, but not catastrophically, below the 1955 level of 15.5 million km² (6 million mi²).

IS IT COLD UP NORTH?

Looking in a bit more detail at recent years (1967 to 2020/2021) what seems to be happening is that the difference in summer and winter ice coverage in the Northern Hemisphere is widening. For example, during the five months from September to January, the amount of snow cover in the Northern Hemisphere has grown by 1% to 2% (500,000 km²) per decade depending on the month.[10] But in the seven months from February to August, the amount of snow cover in the Northern Hemisphere has declined, with the greatest declines in May (down 780,000 km²) per decade and June (down 1.21 million km²) per decade. Overall, this has resulted in a decline of around 1.69% (420,000 km²) per decade.

This difference between the winter months, when snow cover

has been growing, and the summer months, during which snow cover has decreased, allows climate catastrophists to choose the seven summer months to supposedly 'prove' we are heading rapidly towards an ice-melt disaster, while allowing 'deniers' to choose the five winter months to supposedly 'prove' snow and ice cover are actually increasing. In fact, there does seem to be a gradual, but far from disastrous, decline of just 1.69% per decade as would be expected if the Earth has warmed by between 0.6°C and 0.8°C over the last 100 years.

GREENLAND AND ANTARCTICA ARE THE PLACES THAT MATTER

The Arctic sea ice may be a good indicator of variations in the Earth's temperature. But, in spite of the massive media attention Arctic sea ice gets when it either freezes or melts or does neither, in terms of the Earth's total amount of ice, the Arctic isn't that important. The U.S. National Snow and Ice Data Center estimates that ice covers about 15 million square kilometres (km^2). That's around 6 million mi^2, equivalent to about 10% of the Earth's land area and about 3% of the Earth's surface. But the key measurement for ice is the volume of ice which is around 30.5 million cubic kilometres (km^3) for the whole Earth. As the Arctic sea ice is only about two metres thick, there are just 19,200 km^3 of Arctic sea ice – only 0.06% of the Earth's ice volume. Moreover, as it's sea ice, even if it were all to melt, it wouldn't make any difference to the planet's sea levels.

The two most significant accumulations of ice are the Antarctic with about 26 million km^3 (85%) of the planet's ice and Greenland with almost 4 million km³ of ice, around 13%, of the planet's ice. If all the ice in the Antarctic were to melt, that would raise sea levels by a possible 58 metres and if the Greenland ice were to melt, that could raise sea levels by another 8 metres.[11]

GREENLAND USED TO BE A LOT GREENER

There has been a lot of dispute among paleoclimatologists and climatologists and geologists and meteorologists and geophysicists and glaciologists and hydroclimatologists and climate dynamicists and others of their ilk about whether Greenland was ever ice-free in the past and whether it was warmer than today during the Medieval Warm Period from around AD 900 to AD 1300. Some experts have claimed that the Vikings settled in Greenland around AD 985 but abandoned their settlements a few hundred years later due to falling temperatures making agriculture unsustainable. One possible indication of this is that in areas of Greenland where trees now cannot grow, tree roots were found growing through buried bodies:

CHANGING CLIMATE INDICATED IN ARCTIC

Professor Griggs Traces Fate of Lost Norse Colonies to Increasing Greenland Cold.

TREE ROOTS PIERCE BODIES

They Could Not Have Grown in Now Perpetually Frozen Ground, He Holds—Alaska Warmer.

The New York Times
Published: January 22, 1934
Copyright © The New York Times

But other scientists have argued that Greenland did not experience any warming during the Medieval Warm Period and that: 'archaeological evidence points to at least four episodes of extreme hunger while they (the Vikings) were there, with people eating dogs and livestock, all the way down to hides and hooves, several times.'[12]

More recently, it does appear that Greenland experienced significantly higher temperatures than today during the warming that lasted from the 1880s to the 1940s. In December 1939, a Swedish geologist, Professor Hans Ahlmann, made a presentation to the Swedish Geographical Society about a recent expedition to the Arctic in which he claimed:

'All the glaciers in Eastern Greenland are rapidly melting' and 'It may without exaggeration be said that the glaciers – like those in Norway – face the possibility of a catastrophic collapse':

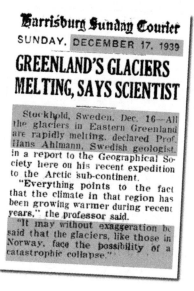

Harrisburg Sunday Courier

SUNDAY, DECEMBER 17, 1939

GREENLAND'S GLACIERS MELTING, SAYS SCIENTIST

Stockhold, Sweden, Dec. 16—All the glaciers in Eastern Greenland are rapidly melting, declared Prof. Hans Ahlmann, Swedish geologist, in a report to the Geographical Society here on his recent expedition to the Arctic sub-continent.

"Everything points to the fact that the climate in that region has been growing warmer during recent years," the professor said.

"It may without exaggeration be said that the glaciers, like those in Norway, face the possibility of a catastrophic collapse."

However, Professor Hans Ahlmann need not have been so worried. Within just a few years of his dire prediction of a 'catastrophic collapse' of Greenland's and Norway's glaciers due to the Earth warming, the warming stopped and the Little Cooling started, which led to the 1960s and 1970s scare about the possible start of a new Ice Age (see Chapter 2 – The 1960s/1970s global cooling scare).

Moreover, a study done in 2007 proposed that the melting of Greenland's ice, when levels of CO_2 in the atmosphere were around 400 parts per million, was nothing unusual as it was just a repeat of what happened in the warming of the 1920s to 1940s when levels of CO_2 in the atmosphere were closer to 300 parts per million:

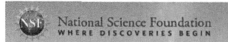

Current Melting of Greenland's Ice Mimicks 1920s-1940s Event

December 6, 2007

Two researchers spent months in Greenland scouring through old expedition logs and reports and reviewing 70 year-old maps and photos before making a surprising discovery: They found that the effects of the current warming and melting of Greenland's glaciers that has alarmed the world's climate scientists, occurred in the decades following an abrupt warming in the 1920s. Full Story

Source
Ohio State University

Makers of natural history programmes like to terrify us with film sequences showing huge lumps of ice breaking off glaciers – calving – and falling into the sea as proof that global warming or climate change or climate crisis is a terrifying threat to humanity which will lead to massive flooding and an environmental disaster.

But on page 16 of his 2010 book *Reporting Live from the End of the World* David Shukman, who was then the BBC's Environment and Science Correspondent, revealed a trick he had been told some film-makers use to get dramatic 'killer shots' of collapsing glaciers. They fly a helicopter near to the edge of a glacier, lower explosive charges into some crevasses, retreat to a safe distance, set up their cameras and then trigger the explosives by remote control. The result is, of course, massive chunks of glacier impressively collapsing into the sea 'proving' global warming is happening and is happening now. The attitude is, as Shukman explains, 'the ice was going to break off sometime anyway, so no big deal.'

Here's a brief section from the BBC's *FROZEN PLANET* documentary of glaciers calving and collapsing into the sea: https://www.youtube.com/watch?v=IQ72d8xYqqQ

Looking carefully at this piece of film, (particularly at around 40 seconds in) it's possible that some people might get the impression that the pieces of collapsing glacier have been 'encouraged' by a series of controlled explosions conveniently timed to give the most dramatic film footage rather than happening naturally as a result of global warming. You can see the ice and snow being thrown up by what could be a series of carefully planned explosions running along the top of the glacier. However, the presenter explains these are 'ruptures deep within the glacier'.

However, if you're still convinced by the climate alarmists' claims that melting Greenland ice will flood the world destroying coastal cities and causing a human and environmental disaster,

you can probably relax. Studies based on 86 ice cores suggest that
the ice covering Greenland has been increasing for at least the last
four hundred years (Figure 9):[13]

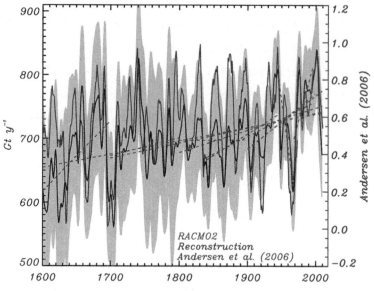

Figure 9 – Greenland net snow accumulation (1600 to 2009)

Moreover, a 12% or 86 gigatonnes per year increase in ice sheet
accumulation rate is found from the end of the Little Ice Age in
about 1840 to the last decade of the reconstruction. This 1840–
1996 trend is 30% higher than that of 1600–2009, suggesting an
accelerating accumulation rate. As for the sharp peaks and
troughs, they were found to have a high level of correlation with
a weather phenomenon called 'The North Atlantic Oscillation
Index' (see Chapter 11 – What about the sun?) and were not
linked in any way to the rise in atmospheric CO_2 levels of the last
hundred or so years.

'NO-GLACIER' NATIONAL PARK?

Wikipedia tells us that: 'Glacier National Park is a 1,583-sq.-mi. wilderness area in Montana's Rocky Mountains, with glacier-carved peaks and valleys running to the Canadian border.' For years, climate alarmists have been warning us that CAGW would soon leave Glacier National Park with no glaciers. The park's glacier-free future was predicted as long ago as 1923:

Medford Mail Tribune (Medford, Oregon) · 29 Dec 1923, Sat

Glacier Park Melting at a Rapid Rate in Scientist's Opinion

CINCINNATI, Dec. 29.—(By the Associated Press)—The hot dry seasons of the past few years have caused rapid disintegration of glaciers in Glacier National park, Montana, professor W. G. Waterman of Northwestern university declared in an address today before the Geological section of the American Association for the Advancement of Science.

Sperry Glacier, studied by Professor Waterman, has lost one-quarter, or perhaps one-third of its ice in the past 18 years, he said. If this rapid retreat should continue, the professor added, the glacier would almost disappear in another 25 years, but he expressed the opinion that the long dry seasons of the past few years is over with probabilities of a lessening in the retreat.

In 1923, we were assured that all the glaciers in the park would be gone by 1948. Then in 1952 we got another warning of the disappearance of the Glacier National Park glaciers by 2002:

The Post-Standard (Syracuse, New York) · 05 Mar 1952, Wed

GLACIERS MELTING

WEST GLACIER, Mont. (Æ)—Montana's Glacier Park may have to start looking for a new name. Naturalists say that 50 years from now it'll be glacierless unless there's a big change in Montana climate. The giant glaciers which gave the park its name are slowly melting away. Some are gone already. Every winter blizzards shriek and swirl around the mountain peaks and replenish the glaciers with new snow, but summer's hot sun take away more than winter adds.

The journalist suggested that the Glacier National Park may need to find a new name given that it wouldn't have any glaciers in the future. A more recent such warning was in the 2 March 2009 edition of the formerly serious *National Geographic*:

NATIONAL GEOGRAPHIC NEWS
No More Glaciers in Glacier National Park by 2020?

Anne Minard
National Geographic News
March 2, 2009

I did a quick check on one of the webcams in the Glacier National Park on Sunday 18 April 2021. There seemed to be a fairly impressive amount of ice and snow:

In fact, the webcam had apparently been playing up a bit recently. But there was so much ice and snow that the park authorities were unable to reach it to check what was wrong. This what they wrote on their website:

'The status of this camera is unknown at this time. It is not accessible this time of year so we will need to wait until we can access the camera to find out the nature of its issues.'

This difficulty reaching the dodgy webcam in April 2021 seemed somewhat surprising given that all the glaciers in the park were meant to have disappeared one year earlier – by 2020. Though, perhaps I'm being a bit impatient. After all, in 2014 the *New York Times* told us that we'll now have to wait till 2044 for all the glaciers in the park to melt:

The New York Times

Climate Change Threatens to Strip the Identity of Glacier National Park

By MICHAEL WINES   NOV. 22, 2014

GLACIER NATIONAL PARK, Mont. — What will they call this place once the glaciers are gone?

A century ago, this sweep of mountains on the Canadian border boasted some 150 ice sheets, many of them scores of feet thick, plastered across summits and tucked into rocky fissures high above parabolic valleys. Today, perhaps 25 survive.

In 30 years, there may be none.

Don't hold your breath. It could be fatal. We've now been waiting almost 100 years since 1923 for Glacier National Park to lose its glaciers. So, the wait continues. Moreover, the supposed 'newspaper' – the *New York Times* – wonders in 2014: 'What will they call this place once the glaciers are gone?' Wasn't that almost exactly the same type of comment a journalist made in the 5 March 1952 New York *Post-Standard* article about the park (see above)? Not only do environmental journalists write rubbish. But often it's not even original rubbish.

ANTARCTIC ICE GETTING THICKER EVERY YEAR

Hopefully readers have not forgotten the (in)famous Antarctic expedition of December 2013 to January 2014. A group of 52 intrepid scientists and tourists set off aboard the Russian ship *Akademik Shokalskiy* to study the melting Antarctic sea ice. First the Russian ship got caught in exceptionally thick pack ice. Then the Chinese ship *Xue Long*, which was sent to rescue the passengers, also got stuck in thick ice. Finally, the *Akademik Shokalskiy's* 52 passengers had to be rescued by helicopter and taken to a third ship, which fortunately wasn't stuck in the thick ice that the climate models predicted shouldn't be there. It could seem almost sad/hilarious when climate catastrophists venture out into reality and find that their models of what should be happening might be more than slightly inaccurate.

By 2016, the Antarctic had gained so much snow and ice that even the normally climate-catastrophist NASA had to admit reality and contradict the 2013 IPCC report which had claimed that the Antarctic was losing ice overall:

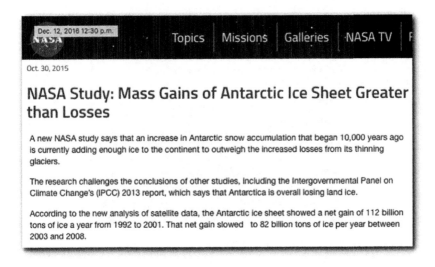

According to NASA's analyses of satellite data:

> 'the Antarctic ice sheet showed a net gain of 112 billion tons
> of ice a year from 1992 to 2001. That net gain slowed to 82
> billion tons of ice a year between 2003 and 2008.'

I read somewhere that the U.S. has recently built its third
Antarctic research station as the first two had disappeared under
the increasing snow and ice. Apparently, new Antarctic research
stations are built on hydraulic stilts that can be extended so they
can be continually raised to cope with the rising snow and ice
levels. I imagine these hydraulic stilts wouldn't be needed if the
Antarctic ice was melting as the climate catastrophists keep
claiming?

In April 2021, climate catastrophists were still warning that the
melting Antarctic ice would be a disaster for mankind and that:
'we need to do something bold':

But in April 2021, Antarctic ice extent (the line in Figure 10 which stops at April) was well above the 1981 to 2010 median (the thick line in Figure 10), massively above the 2017 minimum (the dotted line in Figure 10) and close to the 2015 maximum (the upper line in Figure 10).

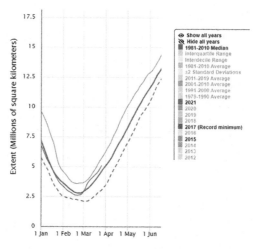

Figure 10 – Antarctic ice sheet in millions km²

In 2008, a leading British scientist predicted that the Earth would soon be so warm that millions of climate refugees would be fleeing to the Antarctic to find somewhere to live:

Given that the temperature in the main part of the Antarctic is normally somewhere around -57°C (-71°F) and given that the Antarctic, far from melting, is adding tens of billions of tons of ice per year, the predicted climate refugees had better make sure they take plenty of warm clothes with them.

THE POLAR BEAR DISASTER THAT DIDN'T HAPPEN

No chapter on melting ice would be complete without mentioning polar bears. For years the key symbol of warming was a lonely polar bear standing on a tiny ice floe:

We're constantly told by the climate alarmists that polar bears face starvation and possible extinction as melting ice has reduced their ability to hunt seals. As is so often the case, the reality may be somewhat different from the alarmists' panicked claims. For a start, polar bears have been around for tens of thousands of years and have comfortably survived over twenty major ice age cycles when temperatures were both much colder and much hotter than they are today.

There is general agreement that now there are nineteen main populations of polar bears. But there is a lot of uncertainty about which populations are declining, which ones are stable and which ones are increasing. Up till 1973, the main danger to polar bear populations was hunting. Then a treaty signed in 1973 limited hunting to about 900 bears a year by local people using traditional methods. Since then the number of polar bears seems to have increased significantly. Some estimates suggest that the polar bear population had gone up from about 12,500 in 1960 to around 26,000 by 2020.[14] Another estimate proposed a rise from about 24,500 in 2005 to over 28,000 by 2019.[15]

In spite of a lack of certainty about population size, what does seem certain is that there hasn't been the disastrous decline in polar bear numbers which the climate catastrophists predicted. Following its failure to become extinct as the doom-predicting mob had confidently expected, the polar bear seems to have been quietly dropped from the climate alarmists' shopping list of impending disasters that would be caused by man-made global warming and may soon be replaced by the walrus. In multi-millionaire Al Gore's follow-up film, *An Inconvenient Sequel*, he seems to have 'forgotten' to mention to his many adoring fans the good news about polar bears thriving.

CHAPTER 4

Rising sea levels?

There appears to be clear evidence that sea levels are rising around the world. Figure 1 shows the sea-level rise at New York.

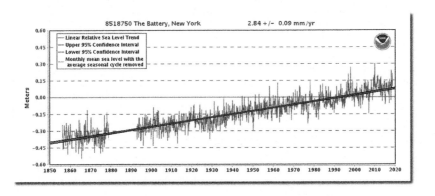

Figure 1 – Sea-level rise The Battery New York (1850 to 2020)

At New York the sea level has been rising at around 2.84 millimetres (mm) a year – 28 cms (just under one foot) every 100 years.

Figure 2 shows a similar trend in sea-level rise at Key West in Florida.

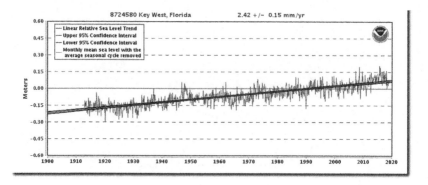

Figure 2 – Sea-level rise Key West, Florida (1900 to 2020)

In Florida the sea level has apparently been rising at a slower rate – 2.42 mm a year – 24.2 cms (about 9½ inches) per 100 years.

But there are more than a couple of problems with the climate alarmists' claims that global warming caused by increasing CO_2 in the atmosphere is leading to these rising sea levels.

PROBLEM I – NO ACCELERATION

If we look at a chart of CO_2 emissions from human activities (excluding land use) we can see that they only really started rocketing upwards after about 1950 (Figure 3). Yet there is none of the acceleration in sea level rise that you would expect if sea levels were directly linked to global warming caused by increasing atmospheric CO_2 levels.

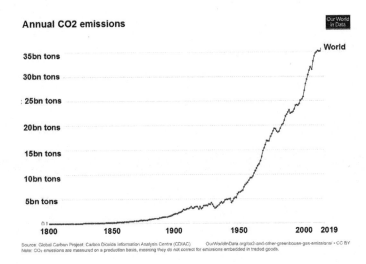

Figure 3 – Annual CO2 emissions from human activities since 1800

You could also make a chart of sea levels compared to levels of atmospheric CO2 (Figure 4). Here I've chosen Hawaii as that's where measurement of atmospheric CO2 levels was first started.

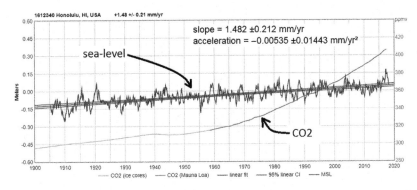

Figure 4 – Sea-level rise vs atmospheric CO2 concentration at Hawaii

This suggests that there is no clear causal link between the rapidly-rising level of CO2 in the atmosphere and the much more constant – 1.482 mm a year – rise in sea levels.

Scientists from NASA have claimed that sea level rise is accelerating from 1.4 mm a year from 1900 – 2000 to 3.4 mm a year since the year 2000:

The Washington Post
Democracy Dies in Darkness

Energy and Environment

Seas are now rising faster than they have in 2,800 years, scientists say

By Chris Mooney
February 22, 2016

A group of scientists says it has now reconstructed the history of the planet's sea levels arcing back over some 3,000 years — leading it to conclude that the rate of increase experienced in the 20th century was "extremely likely" to have been faster than during nearly the entire period.

"We can say with 95 percent probability that the 20th-century rise was faster than any of the previous 27 centuries," said Bob Kopp, a climate scientist at Rutgers University who led the research with nine colleagues from several U.S. and global universities. Kopp said it's not that seas rose faster before that – they probably didn't – but merely that the ability to say as much with the same level of confidence declines.

The study was published Monday in the Proceedings of the National Academy of Sciences.

Seas rose about 14 centimeters (5.5 inches) from 1900 to 2000, the new study suggests, for a rate of 1.4 millimeters per year. The current rate, according to NASA, is 3.4 millimeters per year, suggesting that sea level rise is still accelerating.

But that doesn't seem to be the case at New York or Florida or Hawaii where the sea level rise is fairly constant at somewhere between 2.4 mm and 2.8 mm a year. Moreover, even the Intergovernmental Panel on Climate Change – the high priesthood of the catastrophic global warming alarmist religion – has stated that:

'There is no convincing evidence of an acceleration in global sea level rise during the twentieth century. For longer periods, however there is weak evidence for an acceleration over the last 2-3 centuries.'

WORLD METEOROLOGICAL ORGANIZATION UNITED NATIONS ENVIRONMENT PROGRAMME

INTERGOVERNMENTAL PANEL ON CLIMATE CHANGE

9.3.3 Accelerations in Sea Level Rise

Is there evidence of any "accelerations" (or departures from long-term linear trends) in the rate of sea level rise? From examinations of both composite regional and global curves and individual tide gauge records, there is no convincing evidence of an acceleration in global sea level rise during the twentieth century For longer periods, however, there is weak evidence for an acceleration over the last 2-3 centuries

---

Anyway, even if sea levels are actually rising by NASA's estimated 3.4 mm a year, that would only mean a sea level rise of 34 cms (just over one foot) every 100 years – hardly enough to flood low-lying areas, destroy coastal cities, wipe out whole countries, force tens of millions to flee their homes and cause any great global climatic catastrophe.

PROBLEM 2 – RISING HERE, FALLING THERE?

A second problem with the climate alarmists' claims that increasing atmospheric CO_2 from burning fossil fuels is causing warming which leads to rising sea levels, is that sea levels are not rising everywhere. In fact, at Stockholm (Sweden) sea levels appear to be falling (Figure 5).

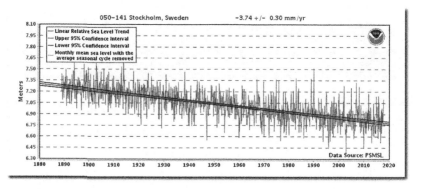

Figure 5 – Stockholm sea-level decline (1880 to 2020)

Sea levels at Stockholm have been falling at a rate of around 3.74 mm a year. So, sea levels have been apparently falling faster at Stockholm in Sweden (- 3.74 mm a year) than they've been rising around the USA (+2.42 mm to +2.84 mm a year) or around Hawaii (+1.48 mm a year).

I don't know anything about the personal hygiene habits of climate alarmists and Extinction Rebellion activists and others of their persuasion. But if they have ever taken a bath, they would know that water seeks a level surface. Theoretically sea-level rises could vary in different geographical locations due to major changes in ocean currents. But any sea-level rises caused by thermal expansion and melting ice due to global warming would be the same at all geographical locations. Yet available data suggests that sea-level rises (and falls) are quite different in different parts of the world. That's the second column of figures which lists sea-level rises and falls in cms per hundred years in Figure 6.

Table 1. Sea level trends, 1880 to 1980, including correction for long-term (6000-year) trends.

Region	Sea level trend, 1880 to 1980			Corrected sea level trend, 1880 to 1980		
	Number of stations	Linear trend (cm/100 years)	95 percent confidence limit (cm/100 years)	Number of stations	Linear trend (cm/100 years)	95 percent confidence limit (cm/100 years)
West coast, North America	16	10	2	1	8	3
Gulf Coast and Caribbean	6	23	4	4	16	5
East coast, North America	32	30	2	30	15	2
Bermuda	1	26	16	1	20	16
West coast, South America	8	19	31	2	-3	3
East coast, South America	5	4	11	2	16	11
Africa	2	32	31	0		
Southern Europe	15	32	2	7	7	2
West central Europe	7	13	2	5	4	2
Southern Baltic	21	4	2	14	5	2
Scandinavia	47	-37*	3*	10	10	3
Asia	9	4	3	2	22	4
Australia	9	13	3	0		
Pacific Ocean	15	19	3	6	6	4
Global mean	193	12	1	86	10	1

*Not included in the global average.

Figure 6 – Sea-level trends 1880 to 1980

What we're actually seeing is that there are changes in sea levels partly due to the warming that has occurred since the 1880s (except for the Little Cooling of the 1960s and 1970s). But the changes, or more accurately apparent changes, in sea levels are also partly due to factors like Tectonic Plate Movement, Glacial Isostatic Adjustment, Post-Glacial Rebound and subsidence due to water abstraction around major cities. Tectonic Plate Movement is, of course, the continual movement of the Earth's tectonic plates which give us earthquakes and tsunamis. Glacial Isostatic Adjustment has been going on for at least two million years. Massive glaciers grow and then melt, alternately depressing the Earth's crust and then releasing it again. As we are now in an interglacial, which has led to melting ice, Scandinavia is slowly rising. Hence, the sea level at Stockholm appears to be falling. In Sweden, for example, a Stone Age camp that used to be by the shore is reportedly now 125 miles from the Baltic Sea.

The Post-Glacial Rebound, which is causing much of the East Coast of North America to sink, occurs because large areas of Canada and America were weighed down by massive ice sheets in the last Ice Age. When that ice melted between 26,500 and 7,000 years ago, land in the centre of the North American began to rise while land around the periphery sank in what has been described as a 'sort of sea-saw effect.'[16] Hence sea levels at the East Coast of America seem to be rising faster than in many other areas of the world. Meanwhile in California on the U.S. West Coast, around 8 million of the state's 40 million inhabitants are believed to live in areas where the land is subsiding probably partly due to Tectonic Movements and partly due to subsidence caused by increased water abstraction.

Looking at the table in Figure 6, one of the largest apparent sea level increases has been 30 cms in 100 years at the East Coast of North America where the land has been sinking due to Post-Glacial Rebound. The sea level for Scandinavia has apparently 'dropped' by 37 cms in 100 years as the land has risen due to Glacial Isostatic rebound. A National Land Survey of Finland study completed in early 2021 calculated that the South Coast of Sweden was rising by at least 1 mm a year, further north the uplift was 2 mm to 3 mm a year and in central Finland the land uplift might be as much as 8 mm to 9 mm a year.

Jakarta is thought to be subsiding by 25 cm a year largely because of groundwater extraction. Houston is sinking as the oil wells beneath it are depleted. Bangkok's and Shanghai's skyscrapers are weighing the two cities down. London is slowly sinking partly due to water abstraction and partly due to Post-Glacial Rebound which is causing Scotland to slowly rise, like Sweden and Finland, after having been weighed down by glaciers during the last ice age.

A report by scientists in 2019 suggested that the real sea level rise due purely to thermal expansion caused by global warming was just 0.7 mm a year:

A realistic expectation of sea level rise in the Mexican Caribbean

Albert Boretti ⚇ ✉

⊞ Show more

https://doi.org/10.1016/j.joes.2019.06.003

Under a Creative Commons license

open access

Highlights

- Sea level rise by thermal expansion is likely less than 0.7 mm/yr.
- Subsidence is main contributor of sea level rise in many areas of the world
- The sea level rise is assessed for Cancun and Playa del Carmen
- The likely relative sea level rise is 67 to 76 mm higher by 2050
- The likely relative sea level rise is 201 to 223 mm higher by 2100

If this estimate is anywhere near accurate, then that's a mere 7 cms every 100 years and probably nothing to cause any real concern. In fact, at that rate it would take almost 9,000 years to reach the

20-foot (6 metre) sea level rise predicted by Al Gore in his shamelessly alarmist 2006 film *An Inconvenient Truth*. Even if sea levels are rising at the 3.4 mm a year (34 cms a century) claimed by climate alarmists at NASA, it would still take over 1,700 years to reach Mr Gore's predicted 20 feet (6 metres) and by that time the climate would probably have changed and the world would have entered at least one cooling phase. One could also wonder how accurate satellite measurements of the constantly moving sea surface taken from 1,300 km to 1,400 km away can be. Can a satellite with a varying orbit really reliably measure sea levels to within a fraction of a millimetre?

In a 2010 documentary called *Earth Under Water* made by the formerly serious *National Geographic*, a whole herd of scientists confirmed that sea levels would rise by 4 feet (1.2 metres) to 6 feet (1.8 metres) by the end of the 21st century and then another 16 feet (4.9 metres) in the 22nd century. The documentary seemed to delight in showing the horrific consequences of flooding of major coastal cities, much of Florida disappearing under the waves, destruction of massive amounts of farmland and tens of millions forced to flee to higher ground. But at the time of writing in April 2021, there are only 79 years left till the end of the 21st century. So, if the sea is rising at 7 cms every hundred years, it would take between 1,700 and 2,600 years (not 79 years) to reach the sea level rises predicted in the *National Geographic* film. Even if sea levels were rising by NASA's most alarmist number of 3.4 mm a year (34 cms a century), it would take between 350 and 530 years. Basically, the film was alarmist rubbish with absolutely no basis in reality. It's amazing that supposed 'scientists' can be found by film-makers to spout such garbage. Surely the supposed 'scientists', while possibly enjoying the ego-enhancing joys of pontificating in front of a camera, must have been aware that their predictions of a 4- to 6-feet sea level rise by the end of the 21st century were pure fantasy?

One of the most enthusiastic proponents of the dangers of catastrophic anthropogenic climate change causing dangerously rising sea levels was former U.S. President Barack Obama. Speaking in 2008, shortly after winning his first presidential election, Obama ominously warned: 'The science is beyond dispute. Sea levels are rising, coastlines are shrinking, we've seen record drought, spreading famine and storms that are growing stronger with each hurricane season.'

Yet, if Mr Obama really believed his own rhetoric about rising sea levels and worsening storms, it's strange that eleven years later, shortly after leaving the White House, former President Barack Obama and his family completed the purchase of a $11.75 million waterfront house situated on nearly 30 acres on Martha's Vineyard – an affluent island located south of Cape Cod in Massachusetts. Not only is Obama's new house near the supposedly rapidly-rising sea, it even has its own private beach.

It would appear that Mr Obama didn't read the 1st October 2019 edition of the *Martha's Vineyard Times* which warned that the island of Martha's Vineyard was already at risk from rising sea levels because: 'According to the Intergovernmental Panel on Climate Change, the average sea level is projected to rise between 12 and 48 inches by 2050 and 12 and 72 inches by 2100.' That would result in regular flooding of coastal properties like the one bought by the Obama family.

Furthermore, around two tropical storms a year usually hit Massachusetts and in 2019 Hurricane Dorian reached Martha's Vineyard after causing devastation in the Bahamas where it was rated as the worst natural disaster in Bahamas's history. The *Martha's Vineyard Times* reported that some areas of the island of Martha's Vineyard were already flooded: 'whenever there is a storm. The select board's concern about future flooding is not unfounded; it is based on numerous studies and well-documented science.' Let us hope that Mr Obama can swim.

In 1989 the *Canberra Times* reported that:

'A Commonwealth Expert Group set up to look at climate change estimated there was a 90 per cent certainty that the planet would become warmer by at least 1-2 degrees, perhaps much more, and that sea levels would rise between one and four metres, by the year 2030.'

THE CANBERRA TIMES, THURSDAY, JANUARY 26, 1989 - 7

Call for anti-greenhouse action

**From JOHN ARDILL,
in London**

GOVERNMENTS must yield national sovereignty to multilateral authorities able to enforce laws "across environmentally invisible frontiers" if the greenhouse effect, which threatens the future of whole nations, is to be overcome, the Commonwealth Secretary-General, Sir Shridath Ramphal, said on Tuesday.

A Commonwealth Expert Group set up to look at climate change estimated there was a 90 per cent certainty that the planet would become warmer by at least 1-2 degrees, perhaps much more, and that sea levels would rise by between one and four metres, by the year 2030. Global warming and sea level rises would continue for decades, perhaps centuries.

There was a prospect of widespread, perhaps catastrophic flooding across large areas of Egypt, India, China, the United States, Britain and Holland, and atolls in the Indian and Pacific oceans.

"Surveys of some of these areas conducted for the Commonwealth Group suggest brutal options. One is the large scale abandonment of land;

conceivably whole countries," Sir Shridath said.

Who would house the displaced populations of low lying areas like the Maldives, a chain of 1200 islands barely above sea level? Current attitudes to refugees and immigrants in most countries did not suggest that large population movements were feasible. Acceptance of an enhanced risk of large scale drowning was clearly not an option. Building defences was simply beyond the means of most poor countries.

"The cost of doing nothing to prevent climate change is simply unacceptable," he said. "But the problems of progressing from collective study to collective action are immense.

"The need to curb emissions of carbon dioxide, the main greenhouse gas, has prompted many environmentalists to advocate a world of slower economic growth. So long as large-scale poverty and rapid population growth remained, this was no solution."

He added, "A large and growing number of environmental issues are cross-border problems which simply cannot be solved nationally. Unless there is a regional or global framework for handling such issues we

will see them escalating dangerously, in some cases to conflict."

Sir Shridath was giving the first of a series of Cambridge lectures on the theme of the Brundtland Report on environment and development. He was a member of the UN commission headed by the Norwegian Premier, Gro Harlem Brundtland, whose 1987 report argued that environmental problems could be tackled successfully only in parallel with economic growth.

"Underlining the report's message of a common future," he said, "is the unspoken premise . . . that we must be ready to nurture tomorrow's concepts of global governance."

This required a change of habit by some of the major powers, which were undermining embryonic forms of multilateral control. An effective law of the sea had been frustrated by the refusal of the US to conform; Russia and Japan had shown a cavalier disregard for the need to observe fishing agreements, and African states were denied a voice in the future of Antarctica.

"Regulation of all the world's commons face similar problems of inequity and unrepresentative control," he added.

— The Guardian

At the time of writing *THERE IS NO CLIMATE CRISIS* in April 2021, there are still nine years to go before the predicted massive rise in sea levels by 2030. But fortunately for Mr Obama and the other wealthy folk who enjoy more than spacious, expensive houses on the coast of upmarket Martha's Vineyard, the scientists' ninety per cent certainty that sea levels will rise by between one and four metres by the year 2030 looks like it will turn out to be one hundred per cent wrong.

Moving to the other side of the world, we were told in 1988 that the 1,196 small islands of the Maldives would disappear under water by 2018:

The Canberra Times

MONDAY, SEPTEMBER 26, 1988

Threat to islands

MALE, Maldives: A gradual rise in average sea level is threatening to completely cover this Indian Ocean nation of 1196 small islands within the next 30 years, according to authorities.

The Environmental Affairs Director, Mr Hussein Shihab, said an estimated rise of 20 to 30 centimetres in the next 20 to 40 years could be "catastrophic" for most of the islands, which were no more than a metre above sea level.

The United Nations Environment Project was planning a study of the problem.

But the end of the Maldives and its 200,000 people could come sooner if drinking water supplies dry up by 1992, as predicted.

— AFP

Here's a picture from a webcam of the Kuredu Island Resort in the Maldives on Sunday 18 April 2021:

The weather doesn't look too great – it seems to be a bit overcast. But the Kuredu Island Resort and all the islands in the distance seem to be doing just fine in spite of the fact that the climate alarmists assured us that they would be well and truly under water about three years before this picture. In fact, despite the climate alarmists' insistence that the Maldives should now be under water, companies from China, India and Saudi Arabia are investing billions in building new infrastructure like bridges and tourist resorts. Moreover, in 2018 a new third and longer runway capable of handling larger jets was opened at the Maldives' main airport and a new $800 million passenger terminal is expected to be completed in 2022 which will increase capacity from one million to 7.3 million passengers a year.

GREAT LAKES GET GREATER

It wasn't just with sea levels that the climate alarmists predicted disaster. In August 2013, a journalist reported:

'It's no secret that, partially due to climate change, the water levels in the Great Lakes are getting very low. It's becoming such a problem that six U.S. Senators from Great Lakes states – Senators Levin, Durbin, Franken, Brown, Schumer and Stabenow – are upset with President Obama for overlooking the Lakes in his Climate Action Plan.'

In their letter to President Obama the senators wrote:

'This year, Great Lakes water levels reached new historic lows severely hampering commercial shipping, jeopardizing recreational boating and fishing, devastating the tourism industry, threatening electric power generation, compromising water supply infrastructure, and exacerbating problems caused by invasive species. In particular, the impacts of climate change on commerce and navigation should be of utmost importance. The Great Lakes Navigation System carries over 160 million tons of cargo annually. Addressing the impacts of climate change on the Great Lakes region is essential for the long-term health, safety, and prosperity of our country.'

The senators were concerned about a plan for Waukesha, a suburb of Milwaukee, to divert nearly eleven million gallons of water a day from Lake Michigan at a time when warming from climate change was believed to have caused evaporation leading to record low water levels. The senators' concerns were echoed in an article on the *Weather Channel* website which detailed the effects of warming on the Great Lakes:

> 'Rising temperatures, extreme weather, damaged ecosystems and rising sea levels are affecting all parts of the world, and the Great Lakes are no exception. Home to 84 percent of North America's surface fresh water and 21 percent of the world's fresh water, the lakes are becoming ever more threatened as the Earth's temperatures continue to rise. The average air temperature in the Great Lakes region has risen by 2 degrees since 1900. In recent years, the Great Lakes' waters have warmed faster than the surrounding air temperature, with Lake Superior warming twice as fast as the air since 1980.'

But our climate can sometimes be a frustratingly obstinate creature as it seems to take pleasure in doing exactly the opposite of what the often mercurial climate catastrophists predicted. Almost as soon as the catastrophists started screaming about an ecological disaster caused by falling water levels in the Great Lakes due to CAGW, the U.S. Geological Survey showed that water levels had stopped falling and had begun rising towards new record levels (Figure 7).

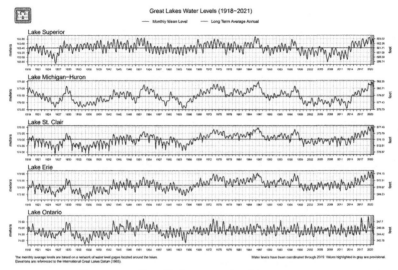

Figure 7 – Great Lakes water levels 1918 to 2021

But the now rising water levels in the Great Lakes probably won't worry the climate alarmists and extinctionists and all their hirsute chums. They know we all have short memories. So, having reliably warned us that man-made global warming was leading to an environmental disaster from low water levels in the Great Lakes, no doubt they'll soon be claiming that man-made global warming will cause an environmental disaster in the Great Lakes area from record high water levels and consequent flooding of the cities and farmland around the shores of the Lakes.

THE BATTLE OF THE CHARTS

Another measure of how CAGW is affecting our seas could be sea temperature. Clearly the warmer our seas become, the more thermal expansion will raise sea levels. But here you can choose charts that show anything you like. For example, here's a chart of the North Atlantic temperature from 1870 to 2010 (Figure 8).

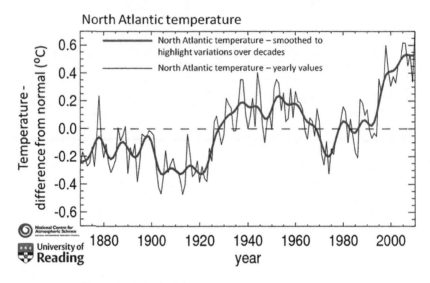

Figure 8 – North Atlantic temperature (1870 to 2010)

We can see that the North Atlantic temperature was below what the researchers called 'normal' from 1870 to 1930. The temperature then remained well above 'normal' following the the hot years up to 1950. It fell again during and following the Little Cooling of the 1960s and 1970s when many scientists predicted a new Ice Age was on the way (see Chapter 2 – The 1960s/1970s Global Cooling Scare). The temperature has been rising apparently to record levels in the warming that has occurred since the 1980s.

The global sea temperature chart published by NOAA (the U.S. National Oceanic and Atmospheric Administration) shows a similar pattern (Figure 9) with sea levels now at record high levels.

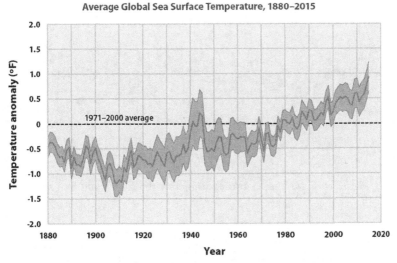

Figure 9 – Average global sea surface temperature (1880 to 2015)

Since 1860, the seawater temperature at the Marsdiep in the Netherlands has been measured daily at 08:00 AM, first at Den Helder and since 1947 from the dike near the jetty of the NIOZ Royal Netherlands Institute for Sea Research. This data series is one of the longest running sets of temperature observations in the Netherlands. Since the year 2000, continuous seawater temperature is also being recorded by electrical sensors. The chart of sea temperature as measured by the Royal Netherlands Institute for Sea Research (Figure 10) shows the same warming since the 1980s seen in Figures 8 and 9. But in the Netherlands chart, temperatures seem to just be heading back to slightly above the levels measured in the 1860s (Figure 10).

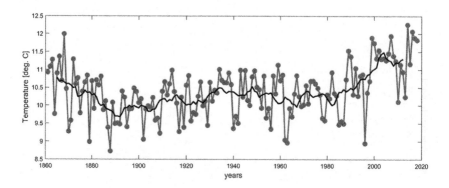

Figure 10 – Sea temperature measured by the NIOZ (1860 to 2019)

The key difference between the Dutch chart and the sea temperature charts from the University of Reading and NOAA is that it starts 10 to 20 years earlier, in the 1860s, and shows a warm period in the 1860s. Looking at the Reading University chart which starts in 1870 and the NOAA chart which starts in 1880 you would conclude that sea temperatures are now at record levels. But looking at the Netherlands chart, you might conclude that sea temperatures have just returned to slightly above their 1860s level. Depending of whether you start your chart at 1880, 1870 or 1860, you could get a quite different impression about whether our oceans are actually reaching the record warm temperatures the alarmists claim.

Moreover, if we look in detail at ocean temperatures for just the most recent years, we can see that ocean temperatures started falling around 2012. Here's the NOAA chart for the North Atlantic (Figure 11)

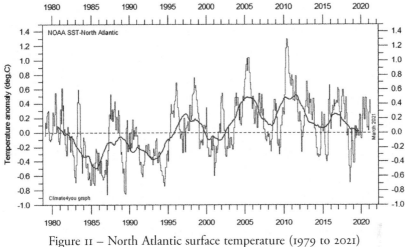

Figure 11 – North Atlantic surface temperature (1979 to 2021)

And here's the NOAA chart for the Tropics (Figure 12)

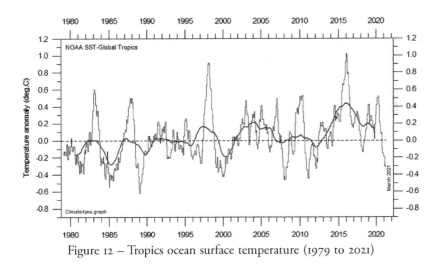

Figure 12 – Tropics ocean surface temperature (1979 to 2021)

Climate phenomena like El Niño and La Niña can cause one-
or two-year fluctuations in sea temperatures. But if ocean
temperatures really were driven mostly by levels of CO_2 in the

atmosphere causing global warming, then it would be theoretically impossible for temperatures to have fallen for the last nine years while atmospheric CO_2 levels were rapidly increasing. This suggests that ocean temperatures are being influenced by something other than atmospheric CO_2 concentrations.

But if you are convinced that ocean temperatures are warming, there are plenty of impressive-looking charts to reinforce your belief (Figure 13)

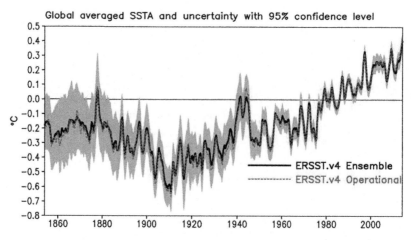

Figure 13 – Ocean surface temperatures vs 20th Century average

However when you look more carefully at such charts, you see that the vertical (y-axis) scale only goes up to a mere 0.5°C and that our oceans have only warmed by 0.6°C in the 160 years since 1860. That's a warming of just 0.4°C per hundred years. That's hardly a number that should inspire terror and end-of-the world predictions. If the y-axis had gone up to say 5°C or even 10°C – an amount of warming which could actually make a difference to the amount of sea ice that could melt or to the quantity of coral reefs that might be harmed – you would hardly see any significant warming at all.

GREAT BARRIER REEF DEFIES CLIMATE ALARMISTS

You may also have been convinced by the catastrophists to lie awake at night tossing and turning as you worried about the survival of the world's coral reefs, in particular the Great Barrier Reef, whose demise has often been forecast. After all, we were warned in 2011: 'the world has only another decade to reduce greenhouse gases to save the Great Barrier Reef.'

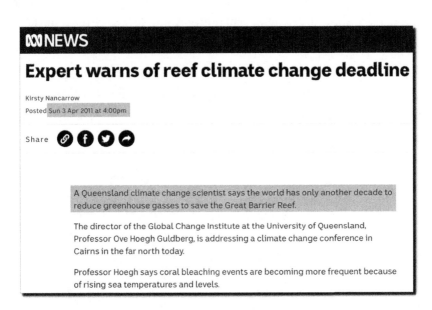

∭ NEWS

Expert warns of reef climate change deadline

Kirsty Nancarrow

Posted Sun 3 Apr 2011 at 4:00pm

Share

A Queensland climate change scientist says the world has only another decade to reduce greenhouse gasses to save the Great Barrier Reef.

The director of the Global Change Institute at the University of Queensland, Professor Ove Hoegh Guldberg, is addressing a climate change conference in Cairns in the far north today.

Professor Hoegh says coral bleaching events are becoming more frequent because of rising sea temperatures and levels.

Since 2011, greenhouse gases have continued to rise. But in April 2021, ten years after the warning of disaster within a decade, the Great Barrier Reef seems to be thriving:

WATERGEDDON? OR JUST A NATURAL POST-GLACIAL WORLD?

Perhaps I should end this chapter on sea levels with four key pieces of data about sea levels. The first is a chart of sea levels since the last glacial period. This is generally accepted by oceanographers and geographers and climatologists and shows that sea levels rose rapidly between about 16,000 to 8,000 years ago and have levelled off since then (Figure 14).[17]

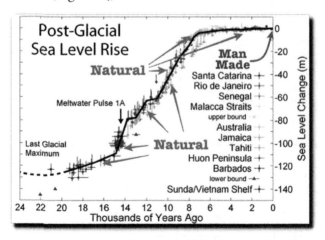

Figure 14 – Post-Glacial sea levels

Hopefully, even climate catastrophists will admit that there were no SUVs and no coal-fired power stations belching out CO_2 during the huge 100-metre post-glacial sea-level rise 16,000 to 8,000 years ago due to natural cyclical warming and ice melt.

Next is a chart of sea levels since 1880, measured mostly by tide gauges and then in the last few decades by satellites (Figure 15).[18]

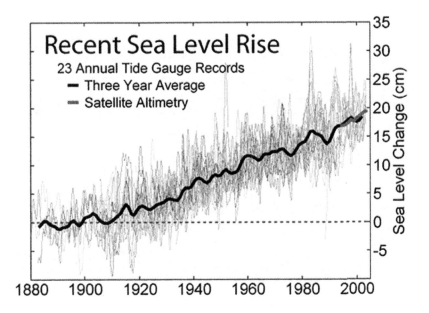

This indicates that sea levels have been rising at a reasonably constant rate of about 2 mm a year – 20 cms every 100 years. At this rate, it would take between 600 and 900 years to reach the 4-feet to 6-feet sea-level rise that the catastrophists have forecast to happen by the end of this century – in 79 years' time.

More recent satellite data (since 1993) suggests that the rate of rise has accelerated to around 3.3 mm a year (Figure 16).[19]

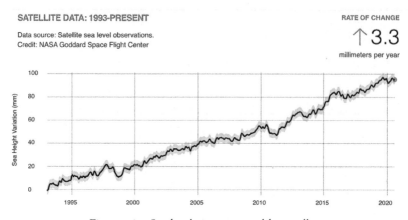

Figure 16 – Sea level rise measured by satellites

At this 3.3 mm a year rate, it would take between 370 and 550 years to reach the 4-feet to 6-feet sea-level rise that the catastrophists have forecast to happen by the end of this century – in just 79 years time.

But giving a different opinion, here's an excerpt from an article on pages 379 to 386 of the *Journal of Ocean Engineering and Science*. This may not be a publication which is on everyone's must-read reading list. But it does seem to be written for real scientists rather than over-passionate climate alarmists and super-excited journalists:

2. The long-term trend tide gauges

Despite many works claim the ocean warming has dramatically accelerated, Zanna et al. [61] the latest, and consequently the sea levels rise at an even larger accelerating rate because of the warming and the melting of ice on land, the empirical evidence behind these claims is, however, missing. Ocean temperature measurements of reasonable quality and coverage are only available since 2005 (ARGO). Tide gauge records, that are an indirect measurement of the ocean heat content, and direct measurement of sea level rise and acceleration, are very scattered especially for the past, and they tell us a different story.

The time series of Rahmstorf [50] or Zanna *et al.* [61] start in 1870. However, not a single tide gauge has been operational since 1870 in the southern hemisphere, and very few tide gauges have been operational since 1870 in the northern hemisphere.

Because of the well-known multi-decadal natural oscillations of periodicity up to quasi-60 years Chambers et al., 2012, Schlesinger and Ramankutty, 1994, not less than 100 years of continuous recording in the same location and without quality issues are needed to compute rates and accelerations by linear and parabolic fittings.

All the long-term-trend (LTT) tide gauges of the world consistently show a negligible acceleration since the time they started recording in the late 1800s/early 1900s, much less than the +0.022 mm/yr^2.

The negligible acceleration of the LTT tide gauges of this world is well-known. As mentioned before, the lack of a significant sea level acceleration has been shown in many works Beenstock et al., 2012, Beenstock et al., 2015, Boretti, 2012a, Boretti, 2012b, Boretti and Watson, 2012, Dean and Houston, 2013, Douglas, 1992, Douglas and Peltier, 2002, Holgate, 2007, Houston and Dean, 2011, Jevrejeva et al., 2006, Jevrejeva et al., 2008, Mörner, 2004, Mörner, 2007, Mörner, 2010a, Mörner, 2010b, Mörner, 2010c, Mörner, 2011a, Mörner, 2011b, Mörner, 2013, Mörner, 2016, Parker, 2013a, Parker, 2013b, Parker, 2013c, Parker, 2013d, Parker, 2013e, Parker, 2014a, Parker, 2014b, Parker and Ollier, 2015, Parker, 2016a, Parker, 2016b, Parker, 2016c, Parker, 2016d, Parker, 2016e, Parker and Ollier, 2017a, Parker and Ollier, 2017b, Parker, 2018a, Parker, 2018b, Parker, 2018c, Parker, 2019, Scafetta, 2014, Schmith et al., 2012, Watson, 2011, Wenzel and Schröter, 2010, Wunsch et al., 2007.

Hence, the state of the oceans cannot be described as sharply warming and accelerating since 1870, as there is yet no sign of the climate models predicted sharply warming and accelerating sea level rise.

The article states that:

'All the long-term-trend tide gauges of the world consistently show a negligible acceleration since the time they started recording in the late 1800s/early 1900s, much less than the

+0.022 mm/year.' And then the article concludes: 'Hence, the state of the oceans cannot be described as sharply warming and accelerating since 1870, as there is yet no sign of the climate models predicted sharply warming and accelerating sea level rise.'

We can't be sure which version of the truth – accelerating sea-level rise caused by anthropogenic CO_2 or negligible sea-level rise due to natural post-glacial warming – is correct. But one thing we can be sure of is that studies contradicting the climate catastrophists' claims of imminent water-logged Armageddon will never be mentioned by any of the mainstream media's supposed 'journalists'. They only seem interested in churning out clickbait, headline-grabbing, end-of-the-world articles pushing the catastrophic anthropogenic global warming scare and dutifully ignore any evidence which casts doubt on the CAGW message of impending doom and disaster caused by mankind's (and, of course, womankind's) greed and selfishness.

CHAPTER 5

Getting hotter?

More than 30 years ago we were warned that CAGW was heating up the Earth and threatening the future of the human race. One of the world's leading climate scientists told us in 1988 that by 2050 temperatures: 'will be 6 to 7 degrees higher.'

Today   Lansing State Journal ■ Monday, Dec. 12, 1988

Prepare for long, hot summers

By EDWARD STILES
Gannett News Service

If you liked last summer's record temperatures, you're going to love the 1990s, says James Hansen, the NASA scientist who, during congressional hearings on the Midwestern drought, linked greenhouse warming to the heat wave.

Last summer was a preview of the average summer 10 years from now, and the hottest summers during the '90s will be even hotter and drier than the one we just struggled through, he says.

Although many scientists argue that the dry, hot summer of '88 was not caused by greenhouse warming, it's hard to find a climate expert who will claim that the greenhouse effect is not on its way.

When Hansen, head of the Goddard Institute for Space Studies, spoke recently to researchers at the University of Arizona Lunar and Planetary Laboratory, he ticked off several unpleasant changes in the weather most scientists agree probably will occur during the next 50 to 60 years:

■ If we do nothing to cut down on pumping carbon dioxide into the atmosphere, temperatures in 2050 will be 6 to 7 degrees higher than they are today. Washington, D.C., for instance, would go from its current 35 days a year over 90 degrees to 85 days a year.

■ The level of the ocean will rise anywhere from one to six feet.

■ The frequency and severity of storms would increase. If the amount of carbon dioxide in the atmosphere doubles — the worst-case scenario between now and 2050 — the maximum strength of hurricanes may increase by 50 percent, Hansen says.

While a few degrees warmer or cooler may not seem like much, such a change can result in huge differences in climate. Hansen notes that during the last ice age the earth was only about 9 or 10 degrees cooler on average than it is now.

He also assured us that by 2050: 'The level of the ocean will rise anywhere from one to six feet.' This was in spite of the fact that ocean levels have probably only risen by about 7 cms per century since measurements began over 100 years ago (see Chapter 4 – Rising sea levels?).

By 2008, the same scientist seemed to be even more hyperbolic with his warnings of impending climate disaster predicting *We're Toast*:

And by March 2021 the UK *Guardian* newspaper seemed to confirm the dire predictions made since the 1980s when the newspaper warned that European heatwaves and drought since 2014 were the worst in 2,000 years: 'The series of severe droughts and heatwaves in Europe since 2014 is the most extreme for more than 2,000 years, research suggests.'

The *Guardian* article went on to claim:

'The heatwaves have had devastating consequences . . . causing thousands of early deaths, destroying crops and igniting forest fires. Low river levels halted some shipping traffic and affected the cooling of nuclear power stations. Climate scientists predict more extreme and more frequent heatwaves and droughts in future.'

The study reported by the *Guardian* in 2021 had apparently: 'Analysed tree rings dating back as far as the Roman empire to create the longest such record to date.' However, if the *Guardian* reporter had bothered to read the *Guardian*'s sister paper, the *Observer*, rather than trusting tree-ring-readers, he could have noticed that his report might well have been more than mildly inaccurate.

In July 1852, an article in the *Observer* detailed a long list of catastrophic hot summers since 1132:

THE OBSERVER, JULY 18, 1852.
STATISTICS OF HOT SUMMERS.

The excessive heat which prevails at present (says a Paris paper) gives some interest to the following account of remarkably hot summers:—"In 1132 the earth opened, and the rivers and springs disappeared in Alsace. The Rhine was dried up. In 1152 the heat was so great that eggs were cooked in the sand. In 1160, at the battle of Bela, a great number of soldiers died from the heat. In 1276 and 1277, in France, there was an absolute failure of the crops of grass and oats. In 1303 and 1304, the Seine, the Loire, the Rhine, and the Danube, were passed over dry-footed. In 1393 and 1394, great numbers of animals fell dead, and the crops were scorched up. In 1440 the heat was excessive. In 1538, 1539, 1540, 1541, the rivers were almost entirely dried up. In 1556 there was a great drought over all Europe. In 1615 and 1616, the heat was overwhelming in France, Italy, and the Netherlands. In 1646 there were fifty-eight consecutive days of excessive heat. In 1678 excessive heat. The same was the case in the first three years of the 18th century. In 1718 it did not rain once from the month of April to the month of October. The crops were burnt up ; the rivers were dried up, and the theatres were closed by decree of the Lieutenant of Police. The thermometer marked 36 degrees Réaumur (113 of Fahrenheit). In gardens which were watered, fruit trees flowered twice. In 1723 and 1734, the heat was extreme. In 1746, summer very hot and very dry, which absolutely calcined the crops. During several months no rain fell. In 1748, 1754, 1760, 1767, 1778, and 1788, the heat was excessive. In 1811, the year of the celebrated comet, the summer was very warm and the wine delicious, even at Suresnes. In 1818 the theatres remained closed for nearly a month, owing to the heat. The maximum heat was 35 degrees (110·75 Fahrenheit.) In 1830, whilst fighting was going on on the 27th, 28th, and 29th July, the thermometer marked 36 degrees centigrade (97·75 Fahrenheit). In 1832, in the insurrection of the 5th and 6th of June, the thermometer marked 35 degrees centigrade. In 1835 the Seine was almost dried up. In 1850, in the month of July, on the second appearance of the cholera, the thermometer marked 34 degrees centigrade. The highest temperature which man can support for a certain time varies from 40 to 45 degrees (104 to 113 of Fahrenheit.) Frequent accidents, however, occur at a less elevated temperature."

These heatwaves included one in 1132 when: 'the earth opened, and the rivers and springs disappeared in Alsace. The Rhine was dried up.' And one in 1303 and 1304 when: 'The Seine, the Loire, the Rhine, and the Danube, were passed over dry-footed.' If you had tried to walk across any of these four rivers during any of the heatwaves this century, you would have got very wet indeed in spite of the *Guardian* journalist's claims of the last few years having the worst droughts for 2,000 years.

Moreover, an article in the July 1884 edition of *Gaillard's Medical Journal* cited extremely hot summers all the way back to the year AD 627:

HOT WEATHER.—Many a man has mopped his brow during the summer months of 1884, declaring it was the hottest weather the world ever knew, which, of course, would not be true, for the extreme heat in the record of the past has not been approached during the late summer.

In 627, the heat was so great in France and Germany, says the *London Standard*, that all springs dried up; water became so scarce that many people died of thirst.

In 879, work in the field had to be given up; agricultural laborers persisting in their work were struck down in a few minutes, so powerful was the sun. In 993, the sun's rays were so fierce that vegetation burned up as under the action of fire. In 1000, rivers ran dry under the protracted heat, the fish were left dry in heaps and putrefied in a few hours. Men and animals venturing in the sun in the summer of 1022 fell down dying.

In 1132, not only did the rivers dry up, but the ground cracked and became baked to the hardness of stone. The Rhine in Alsace nearly dried up. Italy was visited with terrific heat in 1139; vegetation and plants were burned up. During the battle of Bela, in 1200, there were more victims made by the sun than by weapons; men fell down sunstruck in regular rows. The sun of 1277 was also severe; there was an absolute dearth of forage.

In 1303 and 1304, the Rhine, Loire and Seine ran dry. In 1615, the heat throughout Europe became excessive. Scotland suffered particularly in 1625; men and beasts died in scores. Meat could be cooked by merely exposing it to the sun. Not a soul dared to venture out between noon and 4 P.M. In 1718, many shops had to be closed; the theatres were never opened for several months. Not a drop of water fell during six months.

In 1753 the thermometer rose to one hundred and eighteen degrees. In 1779, the heat at Bologna was so great that a large number of people died. In July, 1793, the heat became intolerable. Vegetables were burned up and fruit dried upon the trees. The furniture and woodwork in dwelling-houses cracked and split up; meat became bad in an hour.

In Paris in 1846, the thermometer marked one hundred and twenty-five degrees in the sun. The summers of 1859, 1860, 1869, 1870, 1874, etc., although excessively hot, were not attended by any disaster.

These included the summer of 627 when: 'the heat was so great in France and Germany that all the springs dried up; water became so scarce that many people died of thirst.' In the year 1000: 'Rivers ran dry under the protracted heat, the fish were left dry in heaps and putrefied in a few hours.' Then there was the summer of 1022 when: 'men and animals venturing in the sun fell down dying.' In 1625 the heatwave across Europe was so hot that even normally cold, damp, miserable Scotland: 'suffered particularly; men and beasts died in scores. Meat could be cooked by merely exposing it to the sun. Not a soul dared venture out between noon and 4 P.M.'

More recently, there was the heatwave of 1911 which caused many deaths in Germany, France, Britain and America:

THE BENDIGO INDEPENDENT, FRIDAY, 'AUGUST 11, 1911.

TERRIBLE HEAT WAVE.

OVER 1000 DEATHS IN GERMANY.

BERLIN, Wednesday, August 9.

Upwards of 1000 deaths from sunstroke have occurred in different parts of Germany as a result of the terrific heat wave that has prevailed during the past ten days.

In many cases people who went bathing to obtain relief from the intense heat died of heart failure.

In the valley of the Moselle an epidemic of disease has been caused by decaying fish, which had been netted in shoals. The fish were suffering from a kind of scrofula, due to the overheated state of the water.

In many cities the water supply is available for only two hours daily, and then only for drinking purposes. Even in Berlin street watering has had to be suspended.

Typhus fever and gastritis have been caused in many places through the impaired quality of the water supplied for domestic purposes.

Ice also is running short, and chemists who are ordinarily bound to supply this summer luxury, are now selling it only on the production of a doctor's certificate.

GREAT HEAT IN ENGLAND.

PARIS, Wednesday, August 9.

Severe heat is still being felt in England, the thermometer registering 95 degrees in the shade in London to-day.

Last month was the most rainless July experienced in England for the past 50 years.

LARGE NUMBERS OF DEATHS IN PARIS.

PARIS, Wednesday, August 9.

Owing to a heat-wave in Paris 588 deaths above the normal number have occurred during the past fortnight.

HEAT AND DROUGHT IN AMERICA.

NEW YORK, Thursday, Aug. 10.

The intense heat and drought are seriously affecting the corn and wheat growing areas of the United States.

In the U.S., it was estimated that up to 2,000 people died from the heat just in New England. The New England Historical Society reported that: 'A July 1911 heatwave killed thousands of New Englanders and sent many over the brink of madness.'

A July 1911 heat wave killed thousands of New Englanders and sent many over the brink of madness.

Two men in a park during the 1911 heat wave in New York City. Photo courtesy Library of Congress.

During 11 hellish days, horses dropped in the street and babies didn't wake up from their naps. Boats in Providence Harbor oozed pitch and began to take on water. Tar in the streets bubbled like hot syrup. Trees shed their leaves, grass turned to dust and cows' milk started to dry up.

In every major northeastern city, the sweltering heat drove people to suicide.

On July 4, temperatures hit 103 in Portland, 104 in Boston (a record that still stands), 105 in Vernon, Vt., and 106 in Nashua, N.H., and Bangor, Maine. At least 200 died from drowning, trying to cool off in rivers, lakes, ponds and the ocean – anything wet. Still more died from heat stroke. The 1911 heat wave was possibly the worst weather disaster in New England's history, with estimates of the death toll as high as 2,000.

'During 11 hellish days, horses dropped in the street and babies didn't wake up from their naps. Boats in Providence Harbor oozed pitch and began to take on water. Tar in the streets bubbled like hot syrup. Trees shed their leaves, grass turned to dust and cows' milk started to dry up. In every major northeastern city, the sweltering heat drove people to suicide.'

Of those who died: 'At least 200 died from drowning, trying to cool off in rivers, lakes, ponds and the ocean – anything wet. Still more died from heat stroke. The 1911 heat wave was possibly the worst weather disaster in New England's history, with estimates of the death toll as high as 2,000.' The situation was so bad that some newspapers started reporting the daily deaths from heat:

TOTAL DEATHS IN CITY FROM HEAT.	
Sunday	10
Monday	14
Tuesday	35
Wednesday	43
Thursday	56
Total	158

New York Tribune

In 1930 another deadly heat-wave hit Europe – the worst since 1911:

THE QUEENSLAND TIMES
FRIDAY, AUGUST 29, 1930.

DEATHS REPORTED.

RECORD SINCE 1911.

HEAT WAVE IN ENGLAND

(Australian Cable Service.)
LONDON, August 28.

After weeks of unsettled weather, the greater part of England to-day and yesterday has been sweltering in a heat wave. The shade temperature at 3 o'clock yesterday afternoon was 86 degrees, and to-day at the same hour was 92. This has been the hottest day in August since 1911, when the record temperature of 100 degrees was reached at Greenwich on August 9.

There have only been five other Augusts in this century in which London's temperature has gone into the nineties, and in only two of these was such extreme of heat registered as late in the month as 27th.

A number of heat wave deaths have been reported, including a Grenadier Guardsman, route-marching in Surrey, who sustained sunstroke. There were bathing queues in the Serpentina all day long, and seaside resorts were crowded. The temperature at 9 o'clock to-night was 82 degrees. The heat follows an exceptionally cool and rainy August.

On 29 August 1930, the *Queensland Times* reported from London: 'This has been the hottest day in August since 1911, when the record temperature of 100 degrees was reached at Greenwich on August 9 (1911).' A day later, on 30 August 1930, the UK *Telegraph* newspaper wrote about the heat and deaths in both the UK and France:

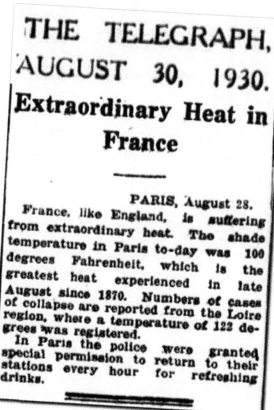

THE TELEGRAPH, AUGUST 30, 1930.

Extraordinary Heat in France

PARIS, August 28.

France, like England, is suffering from extraordinary heat. The shade temperature in Paris to-day was 100 degrees Fahrenheit, which is the greatest heat experienced in late August since 1870. Numbers of cases of collapse are reported from the Loire region, where a temperature of 122 degrees was registered.

In Paris the police were granted special permission to return to their stations every hour for refreshing drinks.

Then there was the terrible heatwave of 1934 in the middle of America's 'Dustbowl' years immortalised in John Steinbeck's novel *The Grapes of Wrath*. In the same year, there was drought in Britain which one newspaper illustrated by showing a picture of a woman standing in a dried-up reservoir:

DROUGHT IN ENGLAND.

England has just experienced the worst drought for nearly 100 years. Above is seen a network of cracks in the dry bed of one of the Tring reservoirs in Hertfordshire.

And there was drought in Australia:

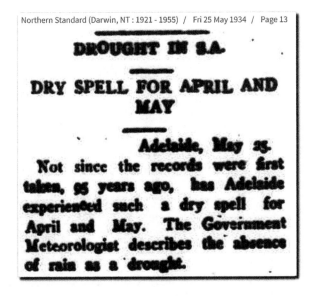

Northern Standard (Darwin, NT : 1921 - 1955) / Fri 25 May 1934 / Page 13

DROUGHT IN S.A.

DRY SPELL FOR APRIL AND MAY

Adelaide, May 25.

Not since the records were first taken, 95 years ago, has Adelaide experienced such a dry spell for April and May. The Government Meteorologist describes the absence of rain as a drought.

The drought also affected Russia:

THE ADVERTISER, ADELAIDE, THURSDAY, MAY 31, 1934

CROP FAILURES IN RUSSIA

More Purchases Of Wheat From Australia

DROUGHT IN GRAIN BELT

Price Of Bread Increased

Special Cables To "The Advertiser"
LONDON, May 29.

The "Daily Telegraph" reports:
—"The Soviet organisation in London is buying Australian and Argentine wheat for shipment to Vladivostock, the Soviet port in Siberia. One Argentine and two Australian cargoes, totalling 22,500 tons, have already been bought and ships chartered for its transport. Further buying is expected.

"Russia's sudden appearance as a buyer is believed to be due to widespread crop failures. In addition, it is probable that wheat consumption in the Vladivostock area has abnormally increased owing to the maintenance of troops there because of tension between Russia and Japan."

The Moscow correspondent of the "Daily Telegraph" reports that a decree announcing a general rise in the price of bread admits for the first time that severe drought has spoilt part of the crop in the southern grain belt.

And South Africa:

THE BARRIER MINER: WEDNESDAY, JANUARY 3, 1934.

GRIPPED BY DROUGHT

South Africa Hard Hit

South African farmers have been severely hit by drought, which has caused an estimated loss of 10 million sheep— about one-fifth of the country's sheep population. The following account of the conditions is given in a letter from the Capetown correspondent of the "Times" under date of September 20:—

Throughout South Africa the people are praying for rain. Almost the whole country is in the grip of a drought, whose like no South African can remember.

There have been disastrous droughts in South Africa before, but in these there has always been some part of the country that has escaped. This time, except for a narrow belt round the coast, the whole country has dried up. The Cape Province has lost thousands of sheep; the Free State is a wilderness of dust storms; the Kruger National Park in the Transvaal has become so dry that the wild animals are trekking in great numbers into Portuguese East Africa in search of water and grazing; in South-West Africa wild animals from uninhabited parts are invading the farms and devouring the little grazing which the farmers have managed to preserve for their stocks. Even the fields of sugar cane in Natal are wilting for lack of rain.

DESPERATE HUNGER

The sheep districts of the Cape and the Free State have felt the drought most. Terrible stories of the hardships of men and animals have come from there. It is the custom in this country, when his grazing and water gives out, for a farmer to take to the road with his flocks in search of pasture. He is allowed by law to graze his sheep for a certain distance— from 100 to 200 yards, according to the district regulations—on each side of the road; and he must move at least six miles a day. Sometimes he rails his stock to districts where he can hire grazing.

In the 2017/2018 U.S. National Climate Assessment, there is a bar chart which supposedly proves that heatwaves are increasing. That's the small bar chart – 2nd chart down – on your left of the picture:

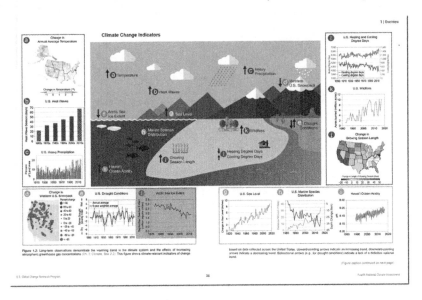

Here is the bar chart in close up (Figure 1).

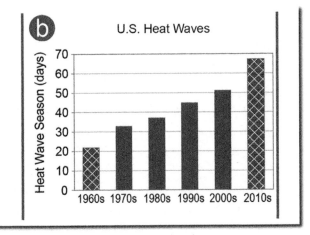

Figure 1 – U.S. heatwaves by decade 1960s to 2010s

The bar chart in the National Climate Assessment conveniently starts in the 1960s. If you go back to the original raw temperature data from all U.S. temperature measuring stations since 1918, you get a completely different picture as the 1920s and 1930s look like they were a lot hotter than any decade during the last 50 to 60 years (Figure 2):

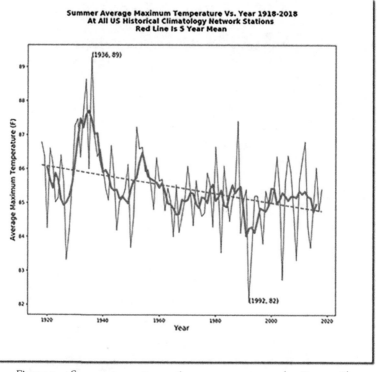

Figure 2 – Summer average maximum temperatures (1918 to 2018)

The fact that the 1920s and 1030s were hotter than any more recent decades is confirmed by the U.S. Environmental Protection Agency (EPA). The EPA Heatwave Index shows a peak in U.S. heatwaves in the 1930s with a smaller peak in the 1950s (Figure 3).

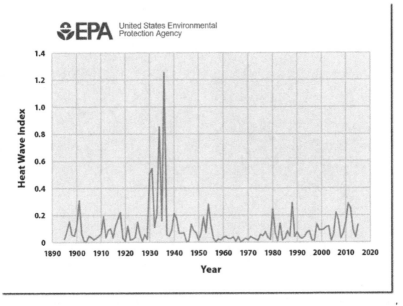

Figure 3 – U.S. EPA Heatwave Index

Similarly, if you look at the percent of days above 95.0° Fahrenheit (figure 4), once again the picture is precisely the opposite of that suggested by the National Climate Assessment bar chart. So, it becomes clear what the National Climate Assessment was trying to achieve by hiding the hot weather prior to the 1960s. By leaving out the much warmer weather of the 1930s and 1950s, the bar chart gives a thoroughly misleading impression of the real temperature changes.

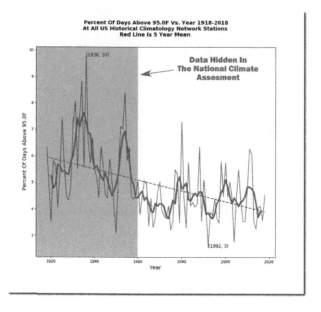

Figure 4 – How the National Climate Assessment hid the warm decades
of the 1930s and 1950s

Almost bordering on the absurd, while showing the bar chart
(Figure 1) supposedly proving heatwaves in the U.S. had been
getting significantly worse over the last 60 years, in the same
2017/18 report, the National Climate Assessment published three
charts – Warmest Temperature, Heatwave Magnitude Index and
Warm Spells in Days – which all show that the 1920s and 1930s
had actually been much hotter that any of the last 60 years:

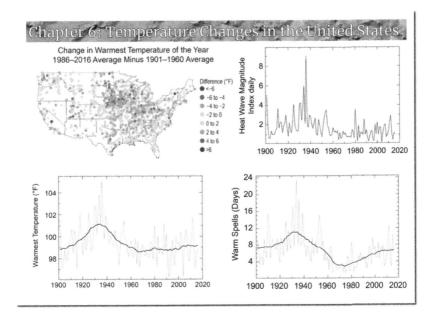

Chapter 6: Temperature Changes in the United States

Unfortunately no journalists seem to have noticed this and so the supposed scientists and journalists kept on plugging the CAGW message that heatwaves were getting hotter and more frequent, when the charts published by the 2017/18 National Climate Assessment clearly showed that the opposite was true.

In summary, despite the claims of over-heated climate alarmists, extinctionists and *Guardian* journalists, heatwaves are not increasing either globally or in the USA. In fact, they appear to be becoming rarer and less severe. And there is just one final point about warming. Most people would naturally assume that warming leads to hotter weather and more droughts. In fact, the opposite may be the case. As about 71% of the Earth's surface is covered by water, warmer air may be causing more thermal-driven evaporation from the oceans creating more clouds and thus increased rainfall of water onto land.

CHAPTER 6

More wildfires?

Wildfires seem to be a favourite of excitable climate activists and impressionable journalists and TV news camera operators. After all, there cannot be any more dramatic, photogenic and telegenic proof of evil, selfish, fossil-fuel-burning mankind turning our planet into a burning fiery furnace than a massive wildfire rushing uncontrollably across the land incinerating forests, houses, cars, wild animals and even people. The two countries which have provided the juiciest wildfire stories of the last few years are the U.S. and Australia:

We've been told repeatedly by the climate alarmists that wildfires in both countries are getting worse and it's all because of man-made global warming. So, I'll look at the climate alarmists' claims about wildfires in both countries and contrast the alarmists' claims with what is really happening.

U.S. — THE CURIOUS CASE OF THE CHEATING CHARTS?

The Fourth U.S. National Climate Assessment written in 2017/18 and published in November 2018 featured a chart showing a massive rise in wildfires in the U.S. since 1983. That's the second chart down on your right-hand side of the central picture:

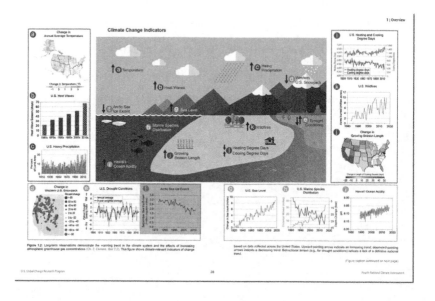

Here's a close-up of the wildfires chart from the National Climate Assessment (Figure 1):

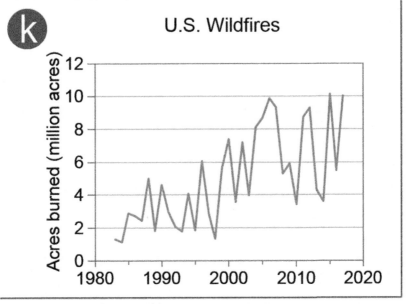

Figure 1 – U.S. wildfires – million acres burned by year 1983 to 2017

The chart appears to show that wildfires are getting worse as the number of acres burned seems to have risen from under two million acres a year to ten million acres a year. That's a five-fold increase. Pretty frightening and definite proof that we're incinerating our long-suffering planet?

JOURNALISTS' VERSION OF THE 'TRUTH'

Reports from some of the USA's most respected newspapers seem to confirm that we're on the path to self-destruction in a heat inferno of our own making. Here's the *Washington Post* from 2 September 2015:

The Washington Post
Democracy Dies in Darkness

Climate and Environment

Wildfires have now burned a massive 8 million acres across the U.S.

 By **Chris Mooney**
Reporter

September 2, 2015 at 3:00 a.m. MDT

This story has been updated.

As of Tuesday, according to the National Interagency Fire Center, more than 8 million acres have burned in U.S. wildfires in 2015. 8,202,557 of them, to be precise. That's an area larger than the state of Maryland.

And the numbers are still growing: 65 large fires are currently raging across the country, particularly in California, Oregon, Washington, Idaho and Montana. That includes three Washington state fires or fire complexes that are larger than 100,000 acres burned.

As of this writing, the United States remains at wildfire preparedness level 5 — the highest level — where it has been since Aug. 13.

There are only six other years that have seen more than 8 million acres burned -- 2012, 2011, 2007, 2006, 2005, and 2004 — based on National Interagency Fire Center records that date back to 1960. It is hard not to notice that all of these years came since the year 2000.

The *Washington Post* informed us that:

'According to the National Interagency Fire Center, more than 8 million acres have burned in U.S. Wildfires in 2015. 8,202,557 of them to be precise.'

The article went on to highlight that such large areas of burning were a recent phenomenon:

'There are only six other years that have seen more than 8 million acres burned – 2012, 2011, 2007, 2006, 2005, and 2004 – based on National Interagency Fire Center records that date back to 1960. It is hard not to notice that all of these years came since the year 2000.'

This story was also picked up by the formerly largely factual *New York Times*:

The New York Times

By MATT RICHTEL and FERNANDA SANTOS APRIL 12, 2016

The 10.1 million acres that burned in the United States last year were the most on record, and the top five years for acres burned were in the past decade. The federal costs of fighting fires rose to $2 billion last year, up from $240 million in 1985.

A leading culprit is climate change. Drier winters mean less moisture on the land, and warmer springs are pulling the moisture into the air more quickly, turning shrub, brush and grass into kindling. Decades of aggressive policies that called for fires to be put out as quickly as they started have also aggravated the problem. Today's forests are not just parched; they are overgrown.

On 12 April 2016, the *New York Times* informed us that: 'The 10.1 million acres that burned in the United States last year were the most on record, and the top five years for acres burned were in the past decade.' And, of course, climate change was to blame:

'A leading culprit is climate change. Drier winters mean less moisture on the land, and warmer springs are pulling the moisture into the air more quickly turning shrub, brush and grass into kindling.'

As with so many recent climate-change disaster articles, it's a pity this journalist doesn't seem to have had either the time or inclination to have read back copies of his own newspaper. If he had bothered to check what his own paper reported about wildfires in the past, maybe he would have come across this article from 9 October 1938?

The New York Times

SUNDAY, OCTOBER 9, 1938.

Forest Fires, One Every 3 Minutes in 1937, Burned 21,980,500 Acres at $20,668,880 Loss

Special to THE NEW YORK TIMES.

WASHINGTON, Oct. 8.—Every three minutes on the average, during 1937, a forest fire started in the United States, but the year's total of losses was considerably under that of 1936.

The Forest Service of the Department of Agriculture reported today that 185,209 forest fires last year burned 21,980,500 acres of timber and caused damage estimated at $20,668,880.

The number of fires in 1937 was 18 per cent less than in the previous year while the burned acreage was only slightly more than half the acreage burned in 1936.

The Service attributed the reduction to more favorable weather, improved fire-fighting technique, better fire detection, more cooperation by private woodland owners, the work of the Civilian Conservation Corps and less carelessness on the part of forest workers and visitors.

Ninety-four per cent of all the acreage burned consisted of unprotected forest areas and more than 11 per cent of all unprotected forested land was burned over. The 121,449 fires on lands not protected burned approximately 20,637,000 acres, causing damage of more than $18,000,000.

The average number of fires annually on unprotected areas during 138,776,000 acres of Federally owned annual loss was 33,129,000 acres valued at $33,613,000.

Fire protection is now given to 130,776,000 acres of Federally owned forest land needing protection, but only three-fifths of the 423,070,000 acres of private and State forest areas needing protection is protected by organized fire control systems.

Fires on Federal land in 1937 were restricted to an average area of 9.5 acres, as compared with the 1933-37 average of 43.3 acres. Fires on private lands showed a reduction from 48.6 acres to 23.1 acres.

Then he would have seen that in 1937, U.S. wildfires burned 21,980,500 acres. That's almost twice the supposed 'record' of 10.1 million acres burned in 2015. Even a numerically-challenged, global-warming-touting journalist/hack (delete as appropriate) from the *New York Times* should be able to understand that 21.98 million acres is rather more than 10.1 million acres.

And if either the *Washington Post* or the *New York Times* journalists had lifted a finger to do a bit of real research before gracing us with their wisdom about supposedly increasing U.S. wildfires, they might even have stumbled on an article about U.S. wildfires from the 23 July 1933 edition of the *Great Falls Tribune* which reported that:

'These statistics indicated destructive fires burn over an acreage of 41,000,000 acres of forest lands each year.'

THE GREAT FALLS TRIBUNE

Sunday Morning, July 23, 1933

WASHINGTON, July 22.—(U.P.)—The reforestation army of 300,000 youths is waging the most extensive campaign in the nation's history to reduce huge annual losses caused by forest fires, insect pests and tree diseases, Robert Fechner, generalissimo of the emergency conservation corps, announced today.

"The need for the work these men are doing is shown by official government figures and reports." Fechner said. "These statistics indicated destructive fires burn over an acreage of 41,000,000 acres of forest lands each year. That 250,000,000 board feet of lumber is killed annually by dark beetles in the California national forests alone and that during the past 10 years, billions of feet of timber have been killed by concentrated attacks of beetles."

WHY START THE CHART IN 1983?

The other problem with the reporting of wildfires centres on why the U.S. National Climate Assessment started their chart of wildfires burned acreage in 1983. A quick search of the Internet takes you to the U.S. National Interagency Fire Center website which explains that:

'Prior to 1983, the federal wildland fire agencies did not track official wildfire data using current reporting processes. As a result there is no official data prior to 1983 posted on this site':

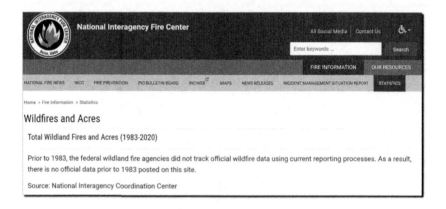

So it seems that the method of collating and reporting wildfire burned acreage changed in 1983. But that doesn't mean that official data weren't collected before 1983. Here's a chart from the United States Department of Agriculture (USDA) Forest Service showing the total acreage burned by year since 1916:

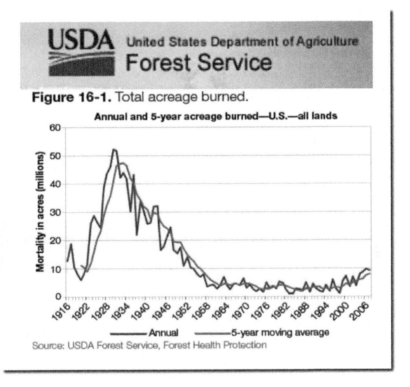

Figure 16-1. Total acreage burned.

It's clear from the USDA Forest Service chart that in the hot 1920s and 1930s (see Chapter 5 – Getting hotter?) burned acreage went as high as 50 million acres in one year. If we look at the long-term trend of burned acreage, we can perhaps see why the 2017/18 Fourth National Climate Assessment report chose 1983 as the starting point for its chart and why it chose to hide all the data before 1983 (the shaded area). The year 1983 was the lowest point for burned acreage in 90 years and after 1983, burned acreage started to rise slightly:

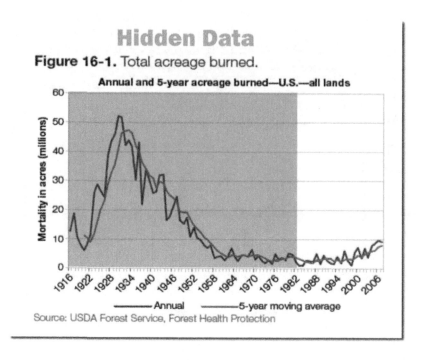

Hidden Data

Figure 16-1. Total acreage burned.

Annual and 5-year acreage burned—U.S.—all lands

Source: USDA Forest Service, Forest Health Protection

One could possibly suspect that the 2017/18 National Climate Assessment wanted to influence journalists and politicians by creating the impression that burned acreage was shooting up to record high levels when, in fact, burned acreage, though slightly increasing was actually at record low levels compared to some years in the 1920s and 1930s.

As for the claim by the *Washington Post* journalist quoted at the start of this chapter that there were record levels of burned acreage this century – 'There are only six other years that have seen more than 8 million acres burned – 2012, 2011, 2007, 2006, 2005, and 2004 – based on National Interagency Fire Center records that date back to 1960. It is hard not to notice that all of these years came since the year 2000.' This is correct in that the *Washington*

Post journalist chose to only use figures from the National Interagency Fire Centre. But had the journalist used data from the Department of Agriculture Forest Service, his story wouldn't have been quite so exciting. In fact, he wouldn't have had a story at all.

And just to conclude this section on wildfires in the U.S., here's a copy of the first section of a 2001 U.S. Government report on Federal Wildland Fire Management Policy:

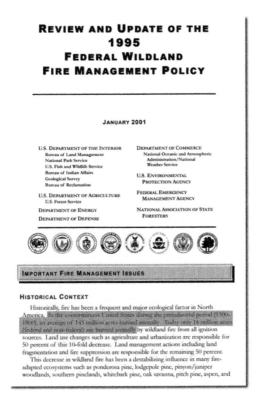

REVIEW AND UPDATE OF THE 1995 FEDERAL WILDLAND FIRE MANAGEMENT POLICY

JANUARY 2001

U.S. DEPARTMENT OF THE INTERIOR
Bureau of Land Management
National Park Service
U.S. Fish and Wildlife Service
Bureau of Indian Affairs
Geological Survey
Bureau of Reclamation

U.S. DEPARTMENT OF AGRICULTURE
U.S. Forest Service

DEPARTMENT OF ENERGY
DEPARTMENT OF DEFENSE

DEPARTMENT OF COMMERCE
National Oceanic and Atmospheric
Administration/National
Weather Service

U.S. ENVIRONMENTAL
PROTECTION AGENCY

FEDERAL EMERGENCY
MANAGEMENT AGENCY

NATIONAL ASSOCIATION OF STATE
FORESTERS

IMPORTANT FIRE MANAGEMENT ISSUES

HISTORICAL CONTEXT

Historically, fire has been a frequent and major ecological factor in North America. In the conterminous United States during the preindustrial period (1500-1800), an average of 145 million acres burned annually. Today only 14 million acres (federal and non-federal) are burned annually by wildland fire from all ignition sources. Land use changes such as agriculture and urbanization are responsible for 50 percent of this 10-fold decrease. Land management actions including land fragmentation and fire suppression are responsible for the remaining 50 percent.

This decrease in wildland fire has been a destabilizing influence in many fire-adapted ecosystems such as ponderosa pine, lodgepole pine, pinyon/juniper woodlands, southern pinelands, whitebark pine, oak savanna, pitch pine, aspen, and

According to this report, the acreage burned in the U.S. by wildfires was much higher in pre-industrial times, when atmospheric CO_2 concentrations were much lower than they are now:

'Historically, fire has been a frequent and major ecological factor in North America. In the conterminous United States during the preindustrial period (1500 – 1800), an average of 145 million acres burned annually. Today only 14 million acres (federal and non-federal) are burned annually by wildland fire from all ignition sources.'

THE AUSTRALIAN BLAME GAME

The 2019-2020 summer fire season in Australia was one of the worst on record in terms of acreage burned and lives lost. Fuelled by record-high temperatures, unusually high winds and prolonged drought, the bushfires affected every Australian state and caused the deaths of 29 people and an estimated more than 1.25 billion animals. Over 46 million acres are believed to have been burned.

But the worst bushfire season by amount of acreage burned seems to have been in 1974/5 when an estimated 117 million hectares (290 million acres) were affected, though only three people died:

Moreover, there have been many other years during which Australia has been devastated by massive bush fires. For example, while only three people were killed in the record 1974/5 fires, 173

died in the 2008/9 fires when only 1.1 million acres burned. In the 1938/9 Australian bushfire season almost five million acres burned and 71 died making 1939 the worst year for fatalities in terms of deaths per hundred thousand of the population (Figure 2).

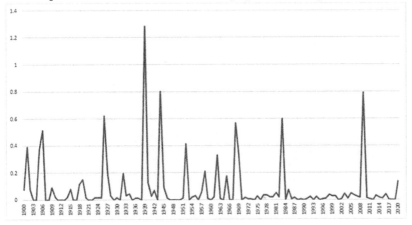

Figure 2 – Bushfire deaths per hundred thousand of the population

By 1940, it was feared that koalas would become extinct due to: 'disease, bushfires, illegal shooting, dogs, foxes, and dingoes.'

Yass Tribune-Courier

MONDAY, AUGUST 19, 1940

KOALAS FACE EXTINCTION

————o————

Of the three families of koalas— the New South Wales, the Victorian and the Queensland—the N.S.W. family is nearest extinction, according to the report of the Koala Club, which was presented to the annual meeting.

The promise of the N.S.W. Government to nationalist koala conservation came to nothing, and the war has made further approach to the Government out of the question for the time, state the president, Mr. O. D. Oberg, and the secretary, Mr. Frank Edwards, in their report.

Some thousands of koalas are still at large in Queensland, but their numbers are dwindling, because of disease, bushfires, illegal shotting, dogs, foxes, and dingoes.

There are 600 of the Victorian race of koalas left.

It's quite difficult to establish what is really happening with the climate in Australia. If you take the official figures released by the Australian Bureau of Meteorology (BOM) with readings starting in 1910, it seems clear that temperatures are rising (Figure 3).

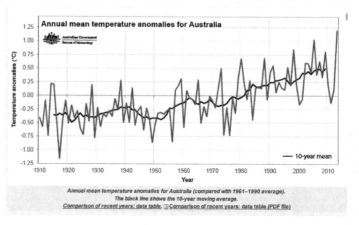

Figure 3 – Australia average mean temperatures since 1910

But if you look at charts made by independent experts starting earlier than the BOM's 1910, you see a quite different picture (Figure 4).

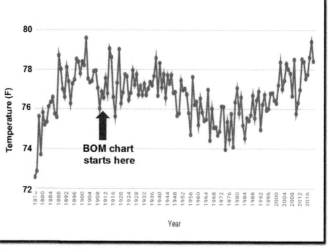

Figure 4 – Daily maximum temperature Australia (1876 to 2017)

This suggests that temperatures in Australia, though rising over the last 60 or so years, are merely returning to levels seen around 1900. This discrepancy between temperature charts has led to suggestions that the BOM uses 1910 as a starting point because that gives the impression of a warming climate by letting them hide the fact that temperatures were warmer before 1910. The small circle on the chart below shows the year 1910 where most charts of Australian temperatures start (Figure 5).

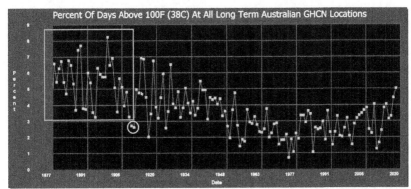

Figure 5 – Percent of days above 100°F (38°C) (1877 to 2020)

The data points in the square box suggest that temperatures may have been significantly higher before 1910.

But if you believe that global warming is increasing Australian temperatures leading to more and worse bushfires, there is a little oddity. Although temperatures seem to have increased by about 1.5°C since 1910 according to the Australian Bureau of Meteorology, rainfall has also been increasing (Figure 6).

Australian annual mean rainfall

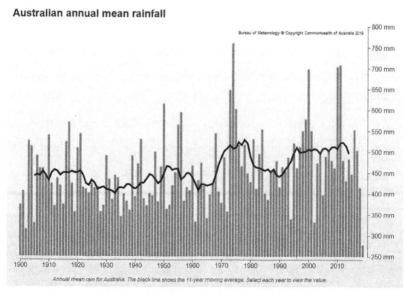

Figure 6 – Australian rainfall since 1900

Yet again, it seems that the climate alarmists' theories – in this case that a warming climate is causing hotter drier weather in Australia leading to droughts and worse bushfires – isn't supported by the facts.

In a particularly dry period from about 2002 to 2008, the Australian newspaper the *Sydney Morning Herald* reported: 'This drought may never break'. And one of Australia's top meteorologists, the Head of Climate Analysis at the Australian Bureau of Meteorology, was quoted as warning: 'perhaps we should call it our new climate.'

smh.com.au

The Sydney Morning Herald

News Entertainment Life & Style Business Sport Travel Tech Other Sections

↳ Home » Environment » Article

This drought may never break

Richard Macey
January 4, 2008

IT MAY be time to stop describing south-eastern Australia as gripped by drought and instead accept the extreme dry as permanent, one of the nation's most senior weather experts warned yesterday.

"Perhaps we should call it our new climate," said the Bureau of Meteorology's head of climate analysis, David Jones.

Yet despite the meteorologist being convinced in 2008 that dry was the new normal, in 2010 and 2011 Australia was deluged under record floods which were so extensive that some oceanographers proposed that they had caused the world's sea levels to drop: 'by as much as 7 mm.'

theguardian

Australian floods of 2010 and 2011 caused global sea level to drop

Puzzled oceanographers who wondered where the sea level rise went for 18 months now have their answer - it went to Australia

An aerial view of flood waters around Wagga Wagga, New South Wales, Australia, on 6 December 2010.
Photograph: Les Smith/pool/EPA

Rain - in effect, evaporated ocean - fell in such colossal quantities during the Australian floods in 2010 and 2011 that the world's sea levels actually dropped by as much as 7mm.

Moreover, what the climate alarmists may have forgotten to tell you was that straight after the terrible, but telegenic, bushfire season of 2019/20, Australia experienced plentiful rainfall which led to a record agricultural season. As the Australian website *Successful Farming* reported:

Australian farmers will harvest a record amount of wheat during the 2020/21 season, the country's chief commodity forecaster said on Tuesday, after heavy rains in the country's key producing regions boosted yields.

With harvesting nearly complete, output will total a record 33.34 million tonnes in the season ending in July 2021, the Australian Bureau of Agricultural and Resource Economics and Sciences (ABARES) said, surpassing the previous all-time high of 31.8 million tonnes in the 2016/17 season. ABARES said in December it expected wheat this year to total 31.17 million tonnes.

The record harvest is a far cry from the production seen in recent years. A three-year drought only ended this year, with many of the areas worst hit, including in the eastern state of New South Wales (NSW), now leading the agricultural recovery. A rebound in the agriculture sector will help the economy to recover from its first recession in 30 years after many businesses were temporarily shut over the past year to slow the spread of COVID-19.

ABARES also increased its forecast for barley production during the 2020/21 season. Production will total 13.1 million tonnes, just shy of the all-time record of 13.4 million tonnes recorded in the 2016/17 season

Although the number of acres burned in 2019/20 does seem to have been well above most previous years apart from 1974/5, there is clear disagreement in Australia about the causes of the large amount of acreage burned. Environmentalists usually link increasing bushfire burned acreage to the rising temperatures caused by global warming. But many Australians believe that increasing restrictions pushed by environmentalists on 'prescribed burning' (Fuel Reduction Burning) – burning deliberately starting fires under controlled conditions to clear out low-lying flammable material – and clearing land to make fire breaks have led to more frequent and more dangerous fires. Figure 7 shows how the acreage burned by prescribed (also called 'controlled') burning has dropped dramatically since 1950 (the top line on the chart) and the area burned by bushfires (the lower line on the chart) has increased.

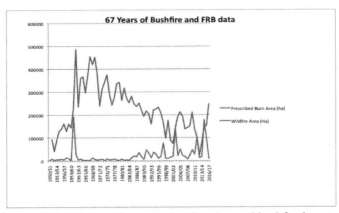

Figure 7 – Area burned by prescribed burning and bushfire burning

Looking at the chart, it is possible to conclude that decreasing prescribed burning has led to increased bushfire burning. Whether this is true or not, there was a well-publicised court case in Australia when a homeowner cleared trees and shrubs within 100 metres of his home in 2002 to create a firebreak in case bushfires ever hit. He was fined Aus $50,000 with another Aus $50,000 in costs for 'illegally clearing trees'. But in the Black Saturday bushfires of 9 February 2009, which killed at least 173 people in Australia, his house was the only one left standing in the small village where he lived.

When interviewed by a local paper he said:

'We wouldn't be around if we hadn't cleared around the house. We were the only ones (in the area) to survive . . . It might not be today and it might not be for ten years, but the reality is it will burn one day. It's Australia, that's what happens.'

During the 2019/20 bushfires which destroyed over 2,400 homes and killed 33 people including 9 firefighters, one volunteer rural firefighter was a bit more forthright with his opinions about increasing pressure from environmentalists to limit prescribed burning and the creation of firebreaks. This was someone who actually had first-hand knowledge of bushfires and how to control them and not a scientist or other supposed 'expert' who spent their days playing with computer models. He was reported as saying:

'People have lost their lives as a direct result of the decisions made by the environmental authorities! Please tell me why these 'enviros' shouldn't be stood up in front of a judge and charged with manslaughter? 'How many more homes? How many more acres of destroyed forest and bushland? How many more lives? How much more do we need to endure until you Muppets realise you f**ked up?'[20]

CHAPTER 7

More extreme weather?

There is no shortage of real experts and self-proclaimed experts warning us that man-made global warming is leading to a dangerous increase in extreme weather events:

'Humanity is sitting on a time bomb. If the vast majority of the world's scientists are right, we have just ten years to avert a major catastrophe that could send our entire planet's climate system into a tail-spin of epic destruction involving extreme weather, floods, droughts, epidemics and killer heat waves beyond anything we have ever experienced – a catastrophe of our own making.'   *– Al Gore*

'The increasing frequency of extreme weather events, droughts and floods is in line with what climate scientists have been predicting for decades – and evidence is mounting that what's happening is more severe than predicted, and will get far worse still if we fail to act.'   *– David Suzuki*

And if there is one thing we can be sure of, it's that extreme weather events like Superstorm Sandy, Typhoon Haiyan in the Philippines, and the British floods – disasters that, combined, pummeled coastlines beyond recognition, ravaged millions of homes, and killed many thousands – are going to keep coming.' – *Naomi Klein*

'Extreme weather events continue to grow more frequent and intense in rich and poor countries alike, not only devastating lives, but also infrastructure, institutions, and budgets – an unholy brew which can create dangerous security vacuums.'   – *Ban Ki-moon*

'We now know that we cannot continue to put ever-increasing amounts of CO_2 into the atmosphere. Actions have consequences. In fact, the consequences of past actions are already in the pipeline. Global temperatures are rising. Glaciers are melting. Sea levels are rising. Extreme weather events are multiplying.'   – *Cary Fowler*

But does the evidence support these claims?

MORE HURRICANES AND TROPICAL STORMS?

If we look at the number of tropical storms (the top line on Figure 1) and hurricanes (the lower line on Figure 1) worldwide over the half century since 1971, both seem to be decreasing very slightly.

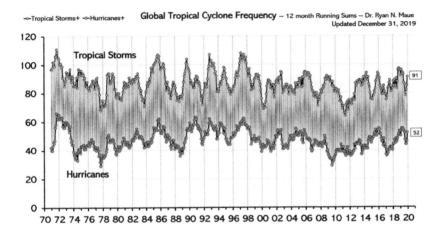

Figure 1 – Tropical storms and hurricanes by year (1971 to December 2019)

If we focus in on the number of landfalling hurricanes in the U.S. since the late 1800s, there is a clear decline (Figure 2)

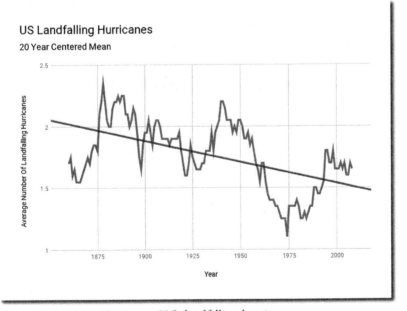

Figure 2 – U.S. landfalling hurricanes

By 2016 there were so few hurricanes that the *Washington Post* newspaper seemed to start panicking about: 'an unprecedented hurricane drought':

The U.S. coast is in an unprecedented hurricane drought — why this is terrifying

By Jason Samenow
August 4, 2016

Hurricanes, large and small, have eluded U.S. shores for record lengths of time. As population and wealth along parts of the U.S. coast have exploded since the last stormy period, experts dread the potential damage and harm once the drought ends.

Three historically unprecedented droughts in landfalling U.S. hurricanes are presently active.

A major hurricane hasn't hit the U.S. Gulf or East Coast in more than a decade. A major hurricane is one containing maximum sustained winds of at least 111 mph and classified as Category 3 or higher on the 1-5 Saffir-Simpson wind scale. (Hurricane Sandy had transitioned to a post tropical storm when it struck New Jersey in 2012, and was no longer classified as a hurricane at landfall, though it had winds equivalent to a Category 1 storm.) The streak has reached 3,937 days, longer than any previous drought by nearly two years.

Fortunately for the *Washington Post*, in 2017 the U.S. was hit by Hurricane Harvey and then in September 2018, Hurricane Florence headed towards the U.S. East Coast. So the *Washington Post* had some hurricanes to write about and, even better, could blame President Trump for the two hurricanes:

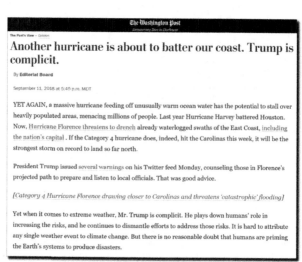

The Post's View • Opinion

Another hurricane is about to batter our coast. Trump is complicit.

By Editorial Board

September 11, 2018 at 5:45 p.m. MDT

YET AGAIN, a massive hurricane feeding off unusually warm ocean water has the potential to stall over heavily populated areas, menacing millions of people. Last year Hurricane Harvey battered Houston. Now, Hurricane Florence threatens to drench already waterlogged swaths of the East Coast, including the nation's capital . If the Category 4 hurricane does, indeed, hit the Carolinas this week, it will be the strongest storm on record to land so far north.

President Trump issued several warnings on his Twitter feed Monday, counseling those in Florence's projected path to prepare and listen to local officials. That was good advice.

[*Category 4 Hurricane Florence drawing closer to Carolinas and threatens 'catastrophic' flooding*]

Yet when it comes to extreme weather, Mr. Trump is complicit. He plays down humans' role in increasing the risks, and he continues to dismantle efforts to address those risks. It is hard to attribute any single weather event to climate change. But there is no reasonable doubt that humans are priming the Earth's systems to produce disasters.

The *Washington Post* wrote: 'Yet when it comes to extreme weather Mr. Trump is complicit. He plays down humans' role in increasing the risks.'

Another way to assess whether typhoons and hurricanes are becoming more extreme could be to look at the death tolls (Figure 3).

Deadliest Pacific typhoons

Rank	Typhoon	Season	Fatalities
1	"Haiphong"	1881	300,000[1]
2	Nina	1975	229,000[1]
3	July 1780 Typhoon	1780	100,000[2]
4	"Swatow"	1922	60,000[1]
5	"China"	1912	50,000[1]
6	July 1862 Typhoon	1862	40,000[2]
7	September 1881 Typhoon	1881	20,000[2]
8	"Hong Kong"	1937	10,000[1]
9	Haiyan	2013	6,340[3]
10	Vera	1959	5,238[1]

Figure 3 – Ten deadliest Pacific typhoons

Seven of the ten deadliest Pacific typhoons happened before 1959 – well before atmospheric CO_2 levels started to rise towards current levels. We see a similar picture with the ten deadliest hurricanes (Figure 4).

Deadliest Atlantic hurricanes

Rank	Hurricane	Season	Fatalities
1	"Great Hurricane"	1780	22,000–27,501
2	Mitch	1998	11,374+
3	Fifi	1974	8,210–10,000
4	"Galveston"	1900	8,000–12,000
5	Flora	1963	7,193
6	"Pointe-à-Pitre"	1776	6,000+
7	"Okeechobee"	1928	4,112+
8	"Newfoundland"	1775	4,000–4,163
9	"Monterrey"	1909	4,000
10	"Dominican Republic"	1930	2,000–8,000

Figure 4 – Ten deadliest hurricanes

Again, seven of the ten deadliest hurricanes were before atmospheric CO_2 reached 350 parts per million.

Whether the two charts of deadliest typhoons and hurricanes (Figure 3 and Figure 4) do actually suggest that their severity is falling could be questioned. On the one hand, you could say that things like better weather forecasting, better detection, more modern communications and improved building standards are mainly responsible for the more recent lower death rates. On the other hand, as the global population has shot up from just 2.5 billion in 1950 to over 7 billion by 2021, many more people are living close to the coast and therefore death tolls from extreme weather should be rising if the weather really was becoming more extreme.

MORE EXTREME TEMPERATURES?

In a recent report, the Intergovernmental Panel on Climate Change (IPCC) wrote:

> 'In summary, since 1950 it is very likely that there has been an overall decrease in the number of cold days and nights and an overall increase in the number of warm days and nights at the global scale, that is, for land areas with sufficient data. It is likely that such changes have also occurred at the continental scale in North America, Europe, and Australia.'

But if we look at the U.S., where we have some of the best long-term temperature records, we can see that the IPCC's claims of more warm days and nights and fewer cold days and nights simply aren't supported by the facts. Figure 5 shows the percent of days per year from 1918 to 2018 where the temperature in the U.S. exceeded 90°F.

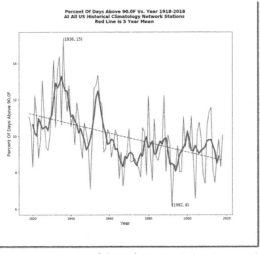

Figure 5 – Percent of days above 90°F (1918 to 2018)

It's clear that the percent of hot days has been falling for the last 100 years. And Figure 6 shows the average minimum temperature by year from 1918 to 2018.

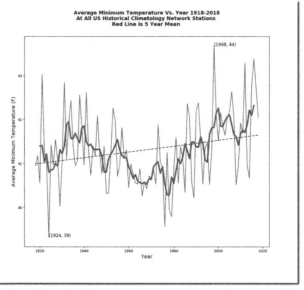

Figure 6 – Average minimum temperature (1918 to 2018)

What seems to be happening in the U.S. is that average maximum temperatures are falling and average minimum temperatures are rising slightly. This would suggest that, if we look at real-world data rather than the computer-modelled capnomancy of the doom-mongering climate catastrophists, the weather in the U.S. appears to be becoming more stable and thus less extreme in spite of increasing atmospheric CO_2.

MORE FLOODS?

Another prediction from climate alarmists and extinctionists is that rising CO_2 levels due to emissions from human activities will lead to more floods. Again the evidence seems to contradict this claim. For example, just in the great floods in China of 1931, an estimated two million are believed to have perished with a further seven million being made homeless:

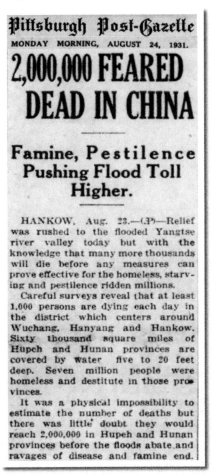

Pittsburgh Post-Gazette

MONDAY MORNING, AUGUST 24, 1931.

2,000,000 FEARED DEAD IN CHINA

Famine, Pestilence Pushing Flood Toll Higher.

HANKOW, Aug. 23.—(P)—Relief was rushed to the flooded Yangtse river valley today but with the knowledge that many more thousands will die before any measures can prove effective for the homeless, starving and pestilence ridden millions.

Careful surveys reveal that at least 1,000 persons are dying each day in the district which centers around Wuchang, Hanyang and Hankow. Sixty thousand square miles of Hupeh and Hunan provinces are covered by water five to 20 feet deep. Seven million people were homeless and destitute in those provinces.

It was a physical impossibility to estimate the number of deaths but there was little doubt they would reach 2,000,000 in Hupeh and Hunan provinces before the floods abate and ravages of disease and famine end.

Yet if we look at over 160 years of rainfall in the Yangtse river basin from 1845 to 2011, there doesn't seem to have been any upwards trend from before industrialisation till the 21st Century (Figure 7).

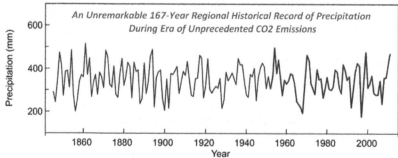

Figure 1. Reconstructed early summer precipitation for the lower Yangtze River Basin over the period 1845-2011. Adapted from Xu et al. (2019).

Figure 7 – Precipitation (mm) Yangtse river basin (1845 to 2011)

Similarly, there have been disastrous floods in the U.S. in the past – the 1930s and 1970s seem to have been particularly bad with major floods in 1913, 1927, 1932, 1936, 1937, 1938, 1972, 1976 and 1977. The flood of 1936 was one of the worst:

But if we look at U.S. rainfall since 1895, there doesn't appear to have been any significant change despite rapidly-rising levels of the much-maligned atmospheric CO2 (Figure 8).

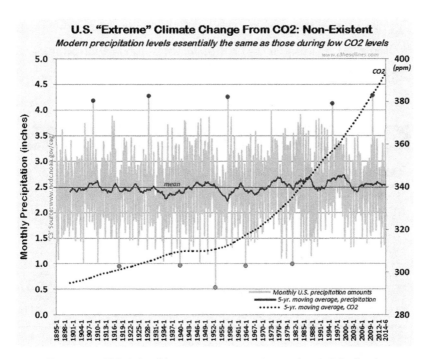

Figure 8 – U.S. Monthly precipitation vs Atmospheric CO2 levels

Rainfall is the flattish line in the centre of the chart and the scale on your left. The atmospheric CO2 level is the rapidly-rising line and the scale on your right.

In 2011, ABC news reported: 'With no end in sight for Texas drought, every farmer in the world will be affected by climate change.' And one scientist was quoted talking about: 'the hellish drought that Texas is now experiencing, and which climate change is almost certainly making worse.' In the same year, the Houston Chronicle in Texas published an article about a new book. The Houston Chronicle wrote:

'as you sit by the pool and sweat this summer, one book you should be reading is "The Impact of Global Warming on Texas".'

The newspaper called the book: 'a sober analysis of our state's vulnerability to climate change' and went on to warn its apparently sweltering readers: 'Get used to it. The weather of the 21st century will be very much like the hot and dry weather of 2011.'

It's true that 2011 was a particularly dry year in Texas. But as seems to happen so often with global warming cultists' augury, as soon as they predict something, the opposite occurs. Figure 9 shows inches precipitation in Texas from 1895 to 2017.

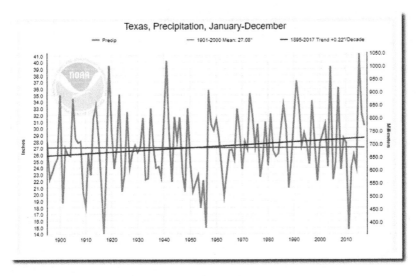

Figure 9 – Precipitation in Texas 1895 to 2017

Sure enough, 2011 was a very dry year. But by 2012, rainfall was almost back to its average level. And by 2015 it started bucketing down and Texas had its wettest year since records began. Overall, precipitation in Texas hasn't been falling. It has been rising at around 0.22 inches per decade for over 100 years. So the climate alarmists' panicky predictions of never-ending droughts in Texas may have been somewhat premature.

And finally, to end this section on rainfall, we could take a third data point from another part of the world – the Amazon basin. In 2015 a newspaper reported: 'Worsening droughts in the Amazon – dubbed 'the lungs of the world' – are speeding up climate change, scientists have warned.'[21] The article was based on a study done by the scientists during a dry spell in 2010.

But if we look at the rainfall chart for the Amazon basin from 1786 to 2018 (Figure 10), we can see the 2010 dry spell. But it is no worse than dry spells in 1832, 1865, 1930-1940, 1960 and 1990 (the lines below the horizontal 'o' line). Moreover, there is no indication that dry spells are increasing in the way that the climate change cultists keep predicting.

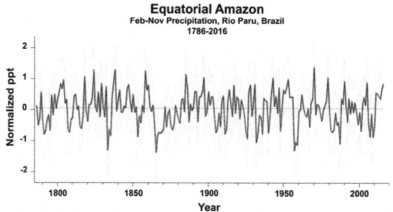

Figure 1. Tree-ring reconstruction of February-November precipitation totals for Rio Paru, Brazil over the period 1786 to 2016 (thick line; blue color for positive or wet years, brown for negative or dry years). The light grey thin lines indicate the 0.05 and 0.95 semi-parametric prediction intervals. Source: Granato-Souza et al. (2019).

Figure 10 – Feb-Nov Amazon precipitation (1786 to 2016)

FROM 'MAD MAX' TO 'WATERWORLD'?

Alarmists like to use Australia as an example of the climatic chaos which will supposedly engulf the world and threaten the human race as atmospheric CO_2 levels rise further. With its frequent droughts and floods, Australia provides plenty of convincing fodder for scientists, activists, journalists and TV crews to spread the terrifying CAGW message. In an article in the British *Guardian* newspaper in March 2021, one of the world's leading climatologists predicted a 'dystopian future' for Australia as catastrophic anthropogenic climate change would cause the weather in Australia to alternate between 'Mad Max' (a barren, drought-blasted wasteland) and 'Waterworld' (a land submerged by floods):

But if the *Guardian's* editor had bothered to do just a little research, he or she or ze might have found a newspaper article from the *Sydney Morning Herald* almost 150 years ago from 4 January 1876 which showed that these predictions that Australia's weather would at some time in the future alternate between drought and flood had already been happening since at least 1789 – that's over 200 years:

THE SYDNEY MORNING HERALD, TUESDAY, JANUARY 4, 1876.

DRY WEATHER.

TO THE EDITOR OF THE HERALD.

SIR,—Observing that Mr. Russell solicits information from private persons which might throw any light on the periodical state of the weather *prior* to 1840, I enclose the herewith table. I have copied it from one of my *scraps*. In one paragraph the writer, Thomas Carter, says, " This table was, for the most part, prepared by Dr. Jevons, and I extracted it from a document in the Sydney Observatory." The rest of his excellent observations may not be pertinent at present, alluding chiefly to the growth of gum trees in swamps, where there was no standing water for a period of fifteen years.

If you think the above worthy a place in your valuable journal, and that it might possibly be of any use to Mr. Russell or others, you will oblige by inserting it.

I am, Sir, your obedient servant,

G. H. C.,
North Shore.

DRY PERIOD.

1789—Drought.	1797—Drought.
1791 „	

WET PERIOD.

1799—Flood.	1812—Flood.
1800 „	1814—Severe drought.
1801 „	1815 „
1805 „	1816—Flood. ”
1806 „	1817 „
1808 „	1818—Slight drought.
1809 „	1819—Flood.
1810 „	1820 „
1811—Flood, slight drought.	1821 „

DRY PERIOD.

1823—Slight drought.	1832—Flood.
1824 „	1835—Slight drought.
1826—Flood. „	1836 „
1827—Flood, severe drought.	1837—Extreme drought.
1828—Severe drought.	1838 „
1829 „	1839 „
1830—Flood. „	1840—Flood. „
1831 „	1841—Slight drought.

WET PERIOD.

1842—Flood.	1852—Flood.
1843 „	1853 „
1844 „	1856 „
1845—Drought.	1857—Flood, slight drought.
1846—Flood.	1859—Flood.
1847 „	1861 „
1848 „	1862 „
1849—Drought.	1863 „
1850—Flood, drought.	1864 „
1851—Flood.	

PART 3

Corruption and lies?

'This disaster is not set to happen in some science fiction future many years ahead, but in our lifetime. Unless we act now . . . these consequences, disastrous as they are, will be irreversible.'

– UK Prime Minister, *Anthony Blair*, 29 October 2006

'If we do not act now, we will witness a scale of global catastrophe the likes of which the world has never seen.'

– Alok Sharma President for COP26*, 14 May 2021

---

* The UK hosts the 26th UN Climate Change Conference of the Parties (COP26) in Glasgow on. 1 – 12 November 2021. The COP26 summit will bring parties together to accelerate action towards the goals of the Paris Agreement and the UN Framework Convention on Climate Change.

CHAPTER 8

Making 'facts' fit the theory?

In this chapter, I propose to look at how temperature records appear to have been deliberately doctored in order to supposedly 'prove' the catastrophic anthropogenic global warming theory. I will deal with two main periods:

1. The last 1,000 or so years where there appear to be contradictions between historical accounts of climatic conditions compared to the claims of the climate alarmists
2. Temperatures since the 1880s where we have clear documented evidence of temperature charts being altered and where we have newspaper reports which directly contradict the claims of the climate alarmists that 21st Century temperatures are higher than they have been for the last 140 years

THE LAST 1,000 YEARS

The first report from the Intergovernmental Panel on Climate Change (IPCC) in 1990 included the following temperature reconstruction for the last 1,000 years:

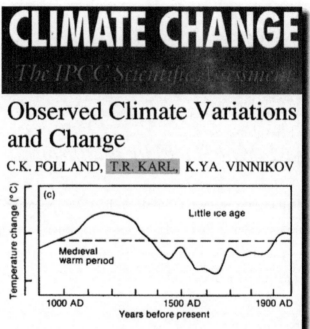

CLIMATE CHANGE

The IPCC Scientific Assessment

Observed Climate Variations and Change

C.K. FOLLAND, T.R. KARL, K.YA. VINNIKOV

Figure 7.1: Schematic diagrams of global temperature variations since the Pleistocene on three time scales (a) the last million years (b) the last ten thousand years and (c) the last thousand years The dotted line nominally represents conditions near the beginning of the twentieth century

Although this chart is just a 'schematic' without any actual temperature values on the vertical axis (the y-axis), it shows two key things – a Medieval Warm Period from about AD 950 to around AD 1400 when temperatures were significantly higher than they were at the beginning of the 20th Century (the dotted line) and a period of cooling which has been called the 'Little Ice Age', even though it wasn't a real ice age, from around AD 1400 to the 1860s.

This view of climate changes during the last 1,000 or so years was confirmed by peer-reviewed studies written by over 750 scientists from 450 research institutions in 40 countries. Moreover, a review of 140 expert studies of the climate history of the past 1,000 years published in *Climate Research* in January 2003 concluded that both the Medieval Warm Period and the Little Ice age had occurred: 'The widespread geographical evidence assembled here supports the existence of both the Little Ice Age and the Medieval Warm Period, and should serve as useful validation targets for any reconstruction of global climate history of the last 1000 yr.'[22] The decision by *Climate Research* to publish the paper reportedly: 'so enraged the advocates of global warming lobby that this provoked a major internal row, resulting in half the ten editors resigning.'[23]

This view of the climate during the last 1,000 or so years accepted by the IPCC in 1990 posed problems for the climate alarmists' conviction that modern warming was mainly caused by rising atmospheric CO_2 levels from burning fossil fuels. After all, the CAGW theory could not explain why temperatures rose above today's levels in the Medieval Warm Period when atmospheric CO_2 was at pre-industrial levels nor why the climate had cooled during the Little Ice Age when atmospheric CO_2 levels remained largely unchanged. Moreover, the chart seemed to suggest that climate changes were cyclical – alternating between warming and cooling – during pre-industrial times and therefore perhaps today's warming was just part of another warming cycle and little or nothing to do with increasing atmospheric CO_2.

But in 1999 the alarmists seemed to hit the jackpot when a group of scientists led by a PhD student, Michael Mann, produced a temperature chart which mainly used tree rings to establish a temperature record for the last 1,000 or so years. This chart indicated that temperatures had been falling from the year AD 1000 to the beginning of the 20th Century when they suddenly started shooting up. The chart became so influential that it even got its own name – 'The Hockey Stick Chart' (Figure 1).

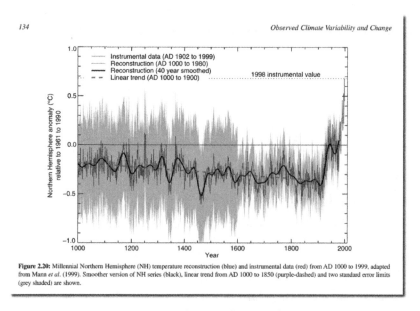

Figure 1 – The Hockey Stick chart

I have to be very careful what I write here as there have been at least two court cases for defamation launched by Mr Mann, now Professor Mann, against people who were more than outspoken in their criticisms of Mr Mann's methods, his use of statistics and his results. There was even a book published in 2015 titled *A Disgrace to the Profession* in which the author interviewed many leading climate scientists about the validity of the Hockey Stick Chart:

The Hockey Stick Chart made both the Medieval Warm Period and the Little Ice Age disappear thus massively strengthening the climate alarmists' message that modern-day warming was something unique, that temperatures were higher now than they have been for over 1,000 years and thus it must be a rise in atmospheric CO_2 from human activities like burning of fossil fuels, rather than any cyclical changes in the Earth's climate, which was responsible for recent temperature rises.

The Hockey Stick got massive publicity and was used extensively in the IPCC's 2001 report. Moreover, the IPCC now changed its story and started claiming that the Medieval Warm Period and the Little Ice Age were just regional climate events and not global:

> Evidence from mountain glaciers does suggest increased glaciation in a number of widely spread regions outside Europe prior to the twentieth century, including Alaska, New Zealand and Patagonia. However, the timing of maximum glacial advances in these regions differs considerably, suggesting that they may represent largely independent regional climate changes, not a globally-synchronous increased glaciation. Thus current evidence does not support globally synchronous periods of anomalous cold or warmth over this interval, and the conventional terms of "Little Ice Age" and "Medieval Warm Period" appear to have limited utility in describing trends in hemispheric or global mean temperature changes in past centuries.

The Hockey Stick Chart became the centrepiece of (possibly self-proclaimed) climate expert Al Gore's 2006 film *An Inconvenient Truth*. But there is a massive amount of historical evidence that both the Medieval Warm Period and the Little Ice Age did happen. Moreover, there is more than a lot of dispute about the methods used in constructing the Hockey Stick Chart, the computer algorithms underlying the chart and the results reached by the (in)famous climate Hockey Stick.

ADJUSTING RECENT HISTORY?

Tampering with the evidence? Exhibit 1

We're on much firmer ground when we look at how data on global temperatures might have been either:

- improved to give a more realistic picture of temperature changes (if you're a climate alarmist)
- massaged to support the CAGW theory (if you're a climate realist).

A good place to start might be a newspaper article from the 26 January 1989 edition of the *New York Times*. This reported that there had been no warming in the U.S. between 1897 and 1987: 'U.S. data since 1895 fail to show warming trend':

We were told that: 'After examining climate data extending back nearly 100 years, a team of Government scientists has concluded that there has been no significant change in average temperatures or rainfall in the United States over that entire period.' The article went on to report that: 'the study was made by scientists for the National Oceanic and Atmospheric Administration.' (NOAA)

Moreover, there was a NASA Science Brief (see Figure 7) published in 1999 which seemed to confirm this lack of warming. The authors wrote:

'In the U.S. there has been little temperature change in the last 50 years, the time of rapidly increasing greenhouse gases – in fact there was a slight cooling throughout much of the country.'

Though the paper does go on to say: 'The last 20 years have seen a slight warming in the U.S.' But if we look at the charts for U.S. temperature now published by NOAA for the period 1895 to 1987, these show a clear warming trend of 0.06°F (0.033°C) per decade – that's the upward sloping line in Figure 2.

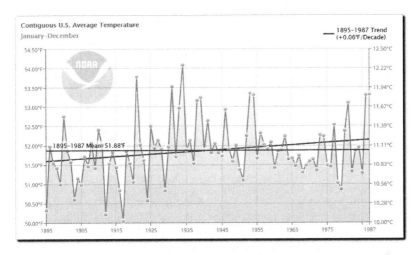

Figure 2 – U.S. temperature 1895 to 1987

So, we have two conflicting reports – one from NOAA in the *New York Times* claiming there has been no warming from 1897 to 1987 – and another one from NOAA from 1895 to 1987 showing there has been a temperature increase of 0.06°F per decade. That's 0.6°F (0.33°C) per century.

Yet in 1986, presumably knowing that, if temperatures were rising at all, they were only rising by a fraction of a degree per 100 years, a leading U.S. climatologist, who could appear to be firmly in the climate alarmists' camp, claimed:

'The average U.S. temperature has risen from 1 to 2 degrees since 1958 and is predicted to increase an additional 3 or 4 degrees sometime between 2010 and 2020.'

12 — THE EVENING TIMES, THURSDAY, JUNE 12, 1986

calculated that if no action is taken to curb chemical emissions, "the greenhouse warming predicted to occur during the next 50 years should be about twice that which has occurred during the previous 130 years."

Hansen said the average U.S. temperature has risen from 1 to 2 degrees since 1958 and is predicted to increase an additional 3 or 4 degrees sometime between 2010 and 2020.

He said that with an expected doubling of atmospheric carbon dioxide by 2040, the number of days each year with temperatures over 80 degrees would rise from 35 to 85 in Washington, D.C., and Omaha, Neb.

Stephen Leatherman of the University of Maryland said that in the last 100 years the sea level has risen about one foot, with about half the increase attributed to global climate warming.

A one-foot rise, he said, generally will produce 100 feet of shoreline erosion on the Atlantic and Gulf coasts. "Within the next 40 to 50 years, sea level will probably have risen by a foot, resulting in major impacts to coastal environments," he said.

Under this projection, the resort town of Ocean City, Md., will lose 39 feet of shoreline by 2000 and a total of 85 within the next 25 years, according to Leatherman.

What this scientist appears to have done was to have chosen a year with low temperatures, 1958, in order to claim significant warming. As for the predicted: 'additional 3 or 4 degrees sometime between 2010 and 2020,' temperatures in the U.S. actually only rose by about 1°F (0.55°C) in total between 1958 and 2020 and not the 4 or 5 degrees in total which the expert had forecast.

Tampering with the evidence? Exhibit 2

The U.S. National Oceanic and Atmospheric Administration issues temperature charts using two types of data:

- 'raw' data which are based on directly measured temperatures
- 'adjusted' data which have apparently been improved to give a more realistic picture of temperatures.

These adjustments are made to compensate for things like movement of measurement stations, changing observation times since 1960 and changes from using liquid-in-glass thermometers to electronic Minimum Maximum Temperature Systems in the 1980s.

Figure 3 shows a chart of the 'raw' (measured) daily maximum temperature data for the U.S. from 1920 to 2020.

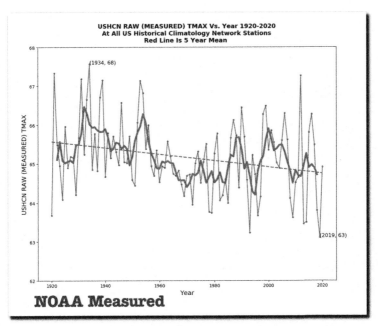

Figure 3 – Raw (measured) temperatures (1920 to 2020)

This shows a clear cooling trend of about half a degree in 100 years. Figure 4 shows the same data, but now adjusted by NOAA to give a more 'realistic' picture of temperature evolution from 1920 to 2020.

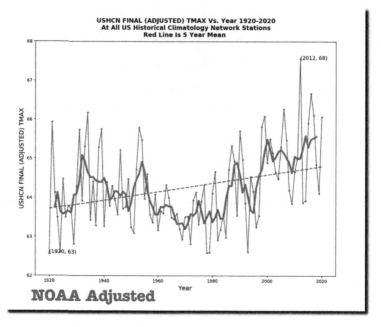

Figure 4 – Adjusted temperatures 1920 to 2020

This now shows a warming trend of about half a degree in 100 years. Moreover, U.S. temperatures from the scorching years of 1921 and 1934 are now apparently much lower than temperatures this century which might seem surprising given the massive death tolls and destruction of agricultural land in first three decades of the 20th Century.

Helpfully the authorities publish a chart showing the differences between the raw (measured) temperatures and the adjusted temperatures (Figure 5).[24] The upper line represents adjustments to maximum temperatures and the lower line shows adjustments to minimum temperatures.

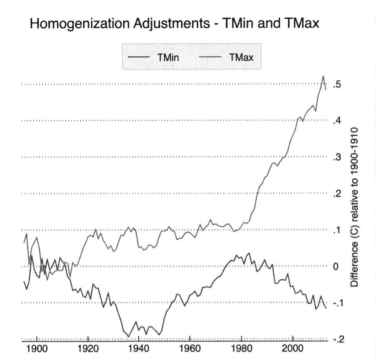

Figure 5 – Adjustments to maximum and minimum temperatures

The most interesting part of this chart is probably the top line – adjustments made to maximum temperatures. We see that adjustments were fairly flat adding about 0.1°C till about 1980. But then there were increasingly large upwards adjustments eventually reaching 0.5°C per year. This boosted maximum temperatures and thus gave a picture of a greater degree of warming than the 'raw' (measured) data reported.

As for minimum temperatures, these have been adjusted down during the hot years of the 1920s and 1930s (when scientists were predicting a global warming catastrophe) to make these years appear colder than they actually were. Then minimum temperatures were adjusted upwards during the cold years of the 1960s and 1970s (when scientists predicted a new Ice Age) to make these cold years appear warmer. So this made warm years look colder and cold years look warmer thus ironing out fluctuations and resulting in a much better fit with the Hockey Stick Chart than the 'raw' (measured) temperatures gave.

Of course, adding a mere 0.5°C to a temperature may not sound like much. But when temperatures are believed to have only increased by between 0.3°C and 0.4°C over the last 50 years, that extra 0.5°C can create warming where there was none, which is obviously extremely useful as convincing evidence for the CAGW theory.

Perhaps all these adjustment were justified. But it does seem oddly convenient that, while the 'raw' (measured) data contradicted the climate alarmists' claims of accelerating atmospheric CO_2-driven warming, the adjusted figures fully supported the climate alarmists' claims of temperatures apparently spiralling upwards out of control.

Tampering with the evidence? Exhibit 3

Hopefully readers aren't suffering from 'chart overdose' as there are a few more to go before the end of this chapter.

Here's a chart of U.S. temperatures from 1880 to 1999 produced by NASA in 1999 (Figure 6). You'll see that the hottest years were 1921 and 1934 when temperatures were well above the 1999 peak.

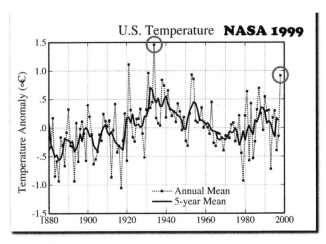

Figure 6 – NASA U.S. temperatures from 1880 to 1999 (1999 version)

We know this chart is genuine because it was published in a 1999 NASA Science Brief (Figure 7) called *Whither U.S. Climate* (the U.S. temperature chart is the chart on your left:):

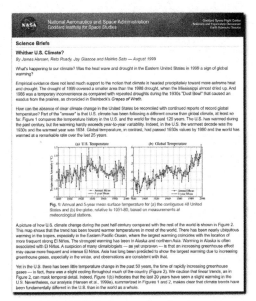

Figure 7 – NASA Science brief – August 1999

This chart makes sense as we know from press reports that in 1921 and 1934 the U.S. suffered from deadly heatwaves (see Chapter 5 – Getting hotter?) But here's the NASA U.S. temperature chart from 1880 to 2000 published in 2019 (Figure 8). You can see that the 1999 temperature peak is now miraculously and comfortably above the previous hottest years of 1921 and 1934.

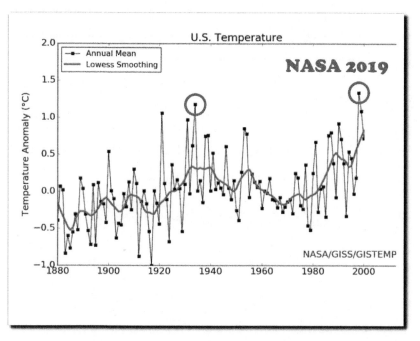

Figure 8 – NASA U.S. temperatures from 1880 to 1999 (2019 version)

Yet data from the U.S. Environmental Protection Agency's Heatwave Index indicate that the 1930s must have been hotter than more recent years (Figure 9).

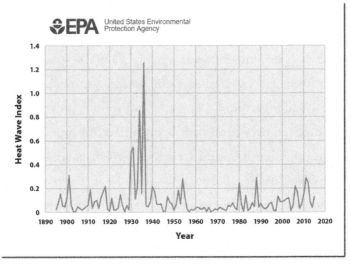

Figure 9 – U.S. EPA Heatwave Index

Moreover, in the 2017/18 U.S. National Climate Assessment, three key indicators of temperature (including the EPA Heatwave Index) all showed that the 1930s were considerably warmer than all the years since U.S. temperatures stated rising after the 1960s and 1970s Little Cooling:

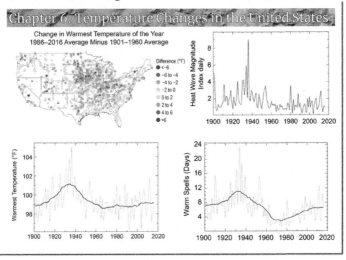

The National Climate Assessment provides the smoking gun which shoots down NASA's attempts to paint 1999 as hotter than the 1930s. If U.S. temperatures were higher in the 1920s and 1930s, when atmospheric CO_2 levels were around 300 parts per million – much lower than today's 417 parts per million, then that might suggest that temperatures were being driven by something other than atmospheric CO_2 and knock an embarrassingly large hole through the CAGW alarmists' claims of CO_2-driven warming. But by making recent temperatures higher than those in the hot 1920s and 1930s, the alarmists' narrative of increasing atmospheric CO_2 driving increasing temperatures can be maintained.

In Figure 10 we can clearly see how daily raw (measured) U.S. temperatures showing a slight cooling trend get transformed into monthly average temperatures showing a clear warming trend.

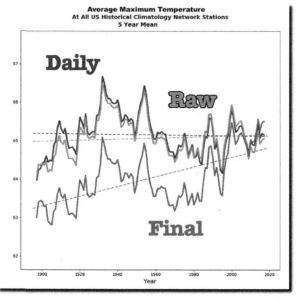

Figure 10 – Adjusting U.S. temperatures from 'raw' to 'final'

Many strange and wonderful things have happened to U.S. temperature charts over the years and curiously they all serve to reinforce the climate alarmists' predictions of CO_2-driven rising temperatures and impending doom.

WHAT ABOUT THE REST OF THE WORLD?

Tampering with the evidence? Exhibit 4

Heat freezes and cold melts?

So far, I have only looked at possible data-fiddling in the U.S. It's difficult to know what has happened to data for the rest of the world as there is very little temperature measurement information available. Here's a map of the distribution of temperature measuring stations worldwide between 1891 and 1920. The shaded areas show where there are the most measuring stations:

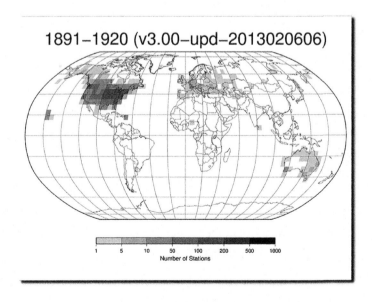

There is little to no coverage in Asia, Africa and South America. In fact, there's almost no monitoring outside the U.S., Europe and Australia. Over half a century later, in 1978, even the now zealously-warmist *New York Times* reported that the situation with land-based measuring stations hadn't improved sufficiently to produce reliable records of global temperatures:

THE NEW YORK TIMES, THURSDAY, JANUARY 5, 1978

International Team of Specialists Finds No End in Sight to 30-Year Cooling Trend in Northern Hemisphere

By WALTER SULLIVAN

An international team of specialists has concluded from eight indexes of climate that there is no end in sight to the cooling trend of the last 30 years, at least in the Northern Hemisphere.

In some, but not all cases, the data extend through last winter. They include sea surface temperatures in the north-central Pacific and north Atlantic, air temperatures at the surface and at various elevations as well as the extent of snow and ice cover at different seasons.

In almost all cases it has been found that the year-to-year variations in climate are far more marked than the long-term trend. The long-term trend often becomes evident only when data from a number of years are displayed.

The report, prepared by German, Japanese and American specialists, appears in the Dec. 15 issue of Nature, the British journal. The findings indicate that from 1950 to 1975 the cooling, per decade, of most climate indexes in the Northern Hemisphere was from 0.1 to 0.2 degrees

Celsius, roughly 0.2 to 0.4 degrees Fahrenheit.

Data from the Southern Hemisphere, particularly south of latitude 30 south, are so meager that reliable conclusions are not possible, the report says. The 30th parallel of south latitude passes through South Africa, Chile and southern Australia. The cooling trend seems to extend at least part way into the Southern Hemisphere but there have been indications of warming at high southern latitudes.

The various indexes were reported as follows:

¶Average surface air temperatures recorded at 358 stations north of latitude 20 degrees south from 1951 to 1975 have been analyzed by Drs. R. Yamamoto and T. Iwashima of Kyoto University in Japan on regional and season bases. A general cooling is evident with "an intensive cooling episode" from 1961 to 1964.

¶Generally similar trends are evident in temperatures of the lower 18,000 feet of the atmosphere as charted by Dr. Horst Dronia of the Weather Office in

Hannover, West Germany. For the period from 1949 to 1976, he has calculated, for 220 points in the Northern Hemisphere, the average temperature of the atmosphere from the separation between the pressure levels near the surface (at 1,000 millibars) and one high up (at 500 millibars). An increase in separation indicated expansion and hence warming. A decrease, for example, of 20 meters (66 feet) was taken to mean atmospheric shrinking, indicating a cooling in that case of 1 degree Celsius (almost 2 degrees Fahrenheit).

¶Observations extending higher into the atmosphere confirmed the trend. The authors were Drs. J. K. Angell and J. Korshover of the National Oceanic and Atmospheric Administration Laboratories in Silver Spring, Md.

¶North Pacific water temperatures compiled by the same agency's Marine Fisheries Service have been analyzed by Dr. Jerome Namias of the Scripps Institution of Oceanography at La Jolla, Calif. The original source was temperature readings of cooling water intake made

The *New York Times* journalist wrote: 'Data from the Southern Hemisphere, particularly south of latitude 30 south, are so meager (sic) that reliable conclusions are not possible.' So, many of the charts of global temperatures have to be constructed by extrapolating what is happening in areas where temperatures are being measured reliably. This leaves an awful lot of room for 'interpretation' and computer modelling to fill in the considerable gaps in geographical coverage of temperatures with whatever the scientists think might have happened or, perhaps more usually, ought to have happened.

As with U.S. temperatures, there seems to be some evidence that charts of global temperatures may also have been rather unsubtly altered to support the man-made global warming message.

In 1974, the U.S. National Centre for Atmospheric Research (NCAR) reported that global temperatures had warmed from just after 1900 to the 1940s, when scientists warned of the threat of global warming (see Chapter 1 – The 1920s/1930s global warming scare). Global temperatures then cooled from the mid-1950s through the 1960s and into the 1970s, when scientists predicted a new Ice Age (see Chapter 2 – The 1960s/1970s global cooling scare).

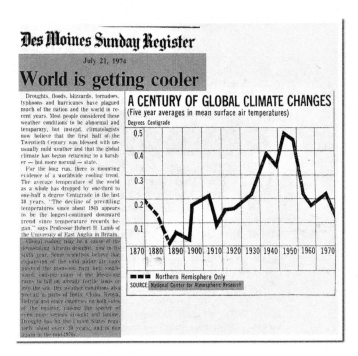

This made sense as we know that glaciers were melting from as early as 1902. This was reported in the *Australian Town and Country Journal*, 16 August 1902:

Australian Town and Country Journal (Sydney, NSW : 1870 - 1907)   Sat 16 Aug 1902   P.

Alpine Glaciers Disappearing.

Hotelkeepers in the Swiss Alps have a new trouble, and are complaining at the loss of patrons. The attractive glaciers are said to be actually passing from the landscape, and as they recede the hotels along their borders find their visitors becoming fewer. These glaciers are not running away, by any means, but they are deteriorating slowly, with a persistency that means their final annihilation. Hotels that a few years ago stood very near to a great river of slowly-moving ice, now find themselves a considerable distance away. The famous glaciers of the Rhone have shrunk several thousand feet in the last 20 years; considerably more than 100ft a year. A number of the well-known glaciers are also shrinking at about the same rate, and the fact is established that these reminders of the great glacial period are certainly disappearing.

Through the 1930s – *New York Times*, 21 December 1930:

The New York Times

SUNDAY, DECEMBER 21, 1930

WORD comes from Switzerland that the Alpine glaciers are in full retreat. Out of 102 glaciers observed by Professor P. L. Mercanton of the University of Lausanne and his associates more than two-thirds have been found to be shrinking. Does this mean the approach of a warmer climate, such as swept over our globe thousands of years ago? Will palms, cypresses, magnolias, myrtles and olive trees thrive at the feet of the Adirondacks, as they did in those distant days?

Into the 1940s – *The Age*,
31 May 1947:

The Age

MELBOURNE, SATURDAY. MAY 31, 1947

MELTING ICE CAP DANGER

Warmer Arctic Temperatures

LOS ANGELES, May 30 (A.A.P.).

A mysterious warming of the climate is slowly manifesting itself in the Arctic, and if the Antarctic ice regions and the major Greenland ice cap should reduce at the same rate as they are at present melting, oceanic surfaces would rise to catastrophic proportions, and people living in the lowlands along the shores would be inundated.

This was the view expressed by Dr. Hans Ahlmann, noted Swedish geophysicist, to-day at the University of California's Geophysical Institute.

Dr. Ahlmann added that temperatures in the Arctic have increased 10 degrees Fahrenheit since 1900, an "enormous" rise from the scientific standpoint.

Then glaciers started growing again in the cooling of the 1960s – the *Canberra Times*, 18 July 1963:

The Canberra Times

CANBERRA: THURSDAY, JULY 18, 1963

Glaciers Grow In Norway

OSLO (A.A.P.-Reuter). —

Norway's glaciers are in the process of becoming thicker again after a period of 200 years of gradually melting down, according to glaciologist, Mr. Olav Liestol.

Moreover, in 1963 there was a large eruption of Mount Agung in Indonesia which killed about 1,600 people and was believed to have cooled the lower atmosphere by as much as 0.5°C

By 1970, the cooling had become so worrying that the U.S. and Soviet Union were investigating:

'Why parts of the Arctic sea ice have recently become ominously thicker and whether the extent of that ice cover contributes to the onset of ice ages.'

— *New York Times*, 18 July 1970

And by 1973, Icelandic ports were blocked by ice.

This all fits in well with the 1880 to 1974 global warming and cooling chart published in 1974:

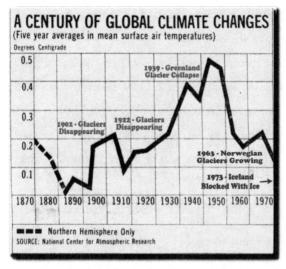

But by 2020, scientists had adjusted the chart of global temperatures. They turned the warming of the 1900s into cooling, reducing the very hot 1920s and 1930s (when scientists at the time predicted melting polar ice and massive flooding of coastal cities) and they all but removed the 20-year Little Cooling of the 1960s and 1970s, when scientists at the time predicted a new Ice Age (Figure 11).

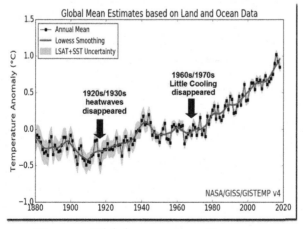

Figure 11 – Global temperatures 1880 to 2019

The 0.5°C cooling from the 1963 Mount Agung eruption also seemed to have disappeared.

This left a temperature chart which appeared to support the mantra that rising atmospheric CO2 was driving global temperatures upwards. But this chart made little sense when compared to reported melting and reforming of glaciers and ice caps from newspaper reports over the 100 years from 1880 to 1980 (Figure 12).

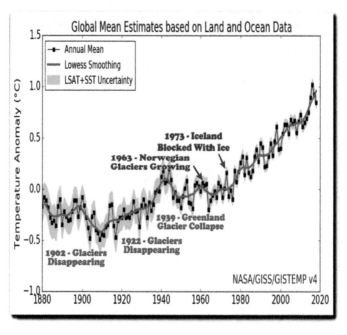

Figure 12 – The misfit between real events and the adjusted temperature chart

For example, with the new 'adjusted' global temperatures chart, we now had glaciers melting and disappearing between 1902 and 1922 when temperatures were (according to the new 'adjusted' chart) plunging to record lows. Then there was more ice melting as temperatures rose up to 1939 when the temperatures were (according to the new 'adjusted' chart) still below average. And even more extraordinarily, the new 'adjusted' chart had glaciers growing and Icelandic ports being blocked by ice when (according to the new 'adjusted' chart) temperatures were at, or even above, average and above the levels where ice had been melting and glaciers disappearing.

Here's a temperature chart which combines two charts from the U.S. National Oceanic and Atmospheric Agency NOAA) of global temperatures from 1880 to 2018. In the line which ends in 1978, we can see the drop in temperature of the 1960s and 1970s Little Cooling. But in the line which ends in 2018, the Little Cooling has been converted into a brief pause in increasing temperature (Figure 13).

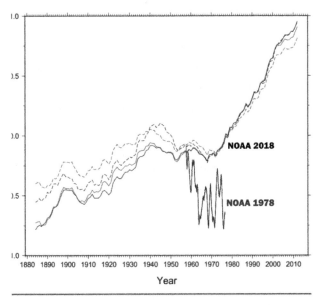

Figure 13 – Global temperatures from NOAA in 1978 and 2018

You can see that NOAA claims global temperatures were below the long-term average in the 1920s and 1930s when the newspaper reports we have from that time show scientists were seriously worried about global warming melting polar ice caps and flooding the world. Then the NOAA chart from 1978 clearly shows a significant drop in temperature during the Little Cooling of the 1960s and 1970s when we know from newspaper reports written at the time that scientists, and even the U.S. CIA, were reporting global cooling and the likely onset of a new Ice Age. But the NOAA 2018 chart has erased the 1960s and 1970s cooling to produce a temperature chart which seems to support the narrative of increasing CO_2 driving increasing temperatures. But the adjusted temperature line simply doesn't make any sense compared to what we know actually happened when we look at contemporaneous newspaper reports.

The climate catastrophists seem to claim that levels of atmospheric CO_2 are a bit like a thermostat in your living room – you increase CO_2 and the temperature goes up, you lower CO_2 and the temperature goes down. The problem with this simplistic cause and effect model is that it didn't explain how temperatures could fall in the 1960s and 1970s when CO_2 levels were increasing (Figure 14).

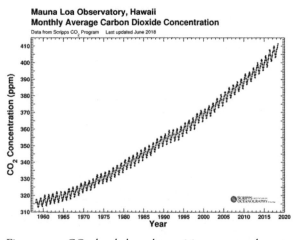

Figure 14 – CO_2 levels have been rising at a regular rate

By cooling the hot weather of the 1920s and 1930s and by eliminating the Little Cooling of the 1960s and 1970s, scientists managed to produce a new global temperatures chart (Figure 15) that seemed to fit wondrously well with the climate alarmists' Chicken Little prophesies of increasing atmospheric CO2 causing catastrophic global warming.

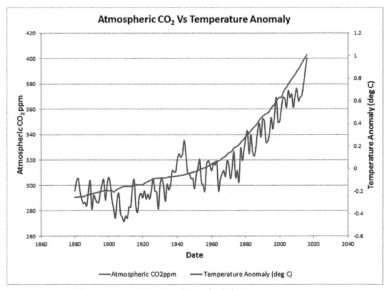

Figure 15 – CO2 levels and global temperatures

But this version of 'reality' contradicted almost 100 years of newspaper reports and scientists' studies about what was actually happening at the time.

TAMPERING WITH THE EVIDENCE? EXHIBIT 5

If we look again at the NOAA chart from Figure 13, we see that global temperatures seem to have risen at a frightening speed since around 1980 (Figure 16)

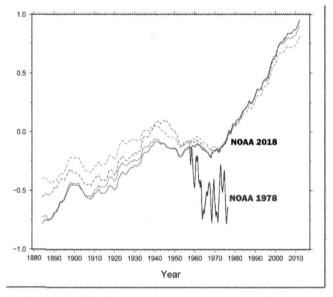

Figure 16 – NOAA shows temperatures continually rising

This is more than strange as charts based on satellite measurements showed a definite pause in warming from 2002 to 2014 (Figure 17).

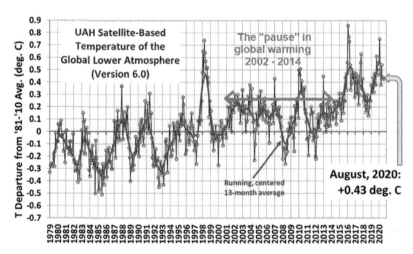

Figure 17– Chart of satellite-recorded temperatures (1979 to August 2020)

We know that this 2002 to 2014 'pause' definitely happened as it was included in the IPCC report and even mentioned by preposterously climate-alarmist media like the BBC:

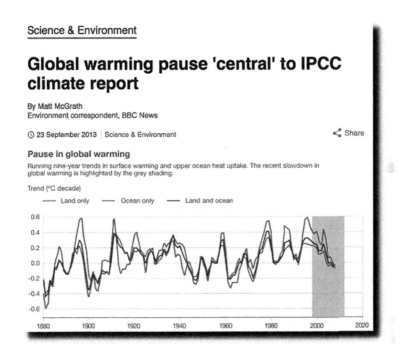

Science & Environment

Global warming pause 'central' to IPCC climate report

By Matt McGrath
Environment correspondent, BBC News

⏱ 23 September 2013 | Science & Environment   ❮ Share

Pause in global warming
Running nine-year trends in surface warming and upper ocean heat uptake. The recent slowdown in global warming is highlighted by the grey shading.

Trend (°C decade)

— Land only   — Ocean only   — Land and ocean

But the pause, which was identified at the time by both the IPCC and the media, represented a problem for the climate catastrophists. After all, how could they claim that CO2 was driving rapidly-rising temperatures, if temperatures stopped increasing for about twelve years while CO2 continued to rise? No problem, they just eliminated the 12-year pause (which we know happened) and changed it into a period of rapid warming (Figure 18).

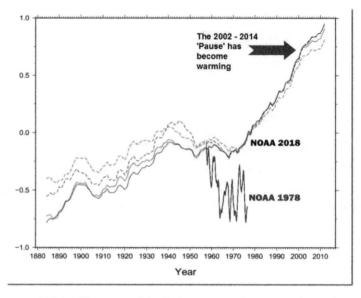

Figure 18 – NOAA 'disappeared' both the 1960s and 1970s Little Cooling and the 2002-2014 Pause

The BBC also changed its mind and in 2015 it decided that the pause, which it had reported in September 2010, had never actually happened:

As supposedly objective official climate monitoring organisations change their charts to cool the hot 1920s and 1930s, to warm up the Little Cooling of the 1960s and 1970s and to 'disappear' the pause of 2002 to 2014, a realist – someone who looks at the evidence before claiming to know the truth – might be tempted to remember another specialist in rewriting history:

URBAN HEAT ISLANDS

Moreover, one could question how accurate land-based temperature measurements can be due to the Urban Heat Island (UHI) effect. As populations have increased and towns have grown, many temperature measuring stations, which were once situated in nice cool countryside, are now surrounded by buildings with heating in the winter and air conditioning in the summer – both of which blast out heat into the surrounding air. Other temperature stations are now in car parks where the tarmac and car exhausts will keep them much hotter than before urban sprawl surrounded them. Similarly, temperature measurement stations near airports will be warmed up by increasing air traffic.

In 1989, an article written by scientists at NOAA and the UK Climate Research Unit concluded that the Urban Heat Island effect might be raising apparent temperatures anywhere between 0.1°C and 0.4°C during the period 1901 to 1984:

Urban Bias in Area-averaged Surface Air Temperature Trends

Thomas R. Karl
NCDC/NESDIS/
NOAA
Federal Building
Asheville, NC 28801

Philip D. Jones
University of East Anglia
Norwich NR4 7TJ,
England

A data set derived from the United States Historical Climate Network has been compared to two global land-based temperature data sets that have been commonly cited in connection with the detection of the greenhouse effect and in other studies of climate change. Results indicate that in the United States the two global land-based temperature data sets have an urban bias between +0.1°C and +0.4°C over the twentieth century (1901–84). This bias is as large or larger than the overall temperature trend in the United States during this time period, +0.16°C/84 yr. Temperature trends indicate an increasing temperature from the turn of the century to the 1930s but a decrease thereafter. By comparison, the global temperature trends during the same period are between +0.4°C/84 yr and +0.6°C/84 yr. At this time, we can only speculate on the magnitude of the urban bias in the global land-based data sets for other parts of the globe, but the magnitude of the bias in the United States compared to the overall temperature trend underscores the need for a thorough global study.

Though by 2020, the committed warmists at CBS had decided that : 'the Urban Heat Islands effect' is real but not very substantial:

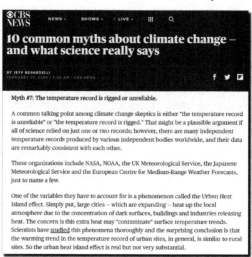

However, the U.S. Environmental Protection Agency (EPA) doesn't seem to agree with the 'climate experts' at CBS. On its website the EPA explains:

'Heat islands are urbanized areas that experience higher temperatures than outlying areas. Structures such as buildings, roads, and other infrastructure absorb and re-emit the sun's heat more than natural landscapes such as forests and water bodies. Urban areas, where these structures are highly concentrated and greenery is limited, become "islands" of higher temperatures relative to outlying areas. Daytime temperatures in urban areas are about 1–7°F higher than temperatures in outlying areas and nighttime temperatures are about 2-5°F higher.'

Clearly, the large increases of several degrees in temperature caused by Urban Heat Islands dwarf the tiny increases in fractions of a degree which the panicking warmists use to try convince us that we are cooking the Earth.

In the UK, the Scottish authorities proudly announced their hottest ever day on 28 June 2018. But it turned out that the heat was coming from the exhaust and refrigerating systems of an ice cream van parked near to the temperature measuring device. This ice cream van seems to have been a highly-effective four-wheeled Urban Heat Island all on its own. Just park it near a temperature measuring station and you immediately had a record warm temperature plus, hopefully, some delicious cooling ice cream.

England's hottest ever day was in a very secluded patch of grass in Cambridge University Botanic Garden in July 2019. The Botanic Garden is sheltered by large buildings whose air conditioning may have contributed more than slightly to the supposed record temperature high. And in Germany, the country's hottest temperature was reportedly in a town called Lingen recorded by a temperature measuring station in a well-sheltered dip in the ground. Yet this apparent temperature record wasn't picked up by any of the temperature measuring stations in six nearby towns. The top line on the table below is the temperature at Lingen. The other lines are temperatures at six nearby weather stations:

Max temperature [°C] comparison between Lingen and 6 nearby stations

Station	23 July	24 July	25 July	26 July	27 July
Lingen	35.8	39.1	42.6	37.7	34.0
Nordhorn	33.7	36.5	40.9	36.1	32.9
Meppen	32.4	36.6	39.7	34.1	30.2
Ahaus	33.1	37.3	39.5	26.3	32.3
Diepholz	32.9	36.7	39.0	34.6	30.8
Bersenbrück	32.8	36.8	39.3	33.2	31.0
Emsdetten	33.9	38.0	40.6	36.6	32.8

CHAPTER 9

The '97% of scientists agree' claim

Probably one of the most repeated arguments you'll hear, over and over again, in support of the CAGW cult is that 97% of scientists agree that CAGW is happening.

President Obama is just one of many who have made this claim: 'Ninety-seven percent of scientists agree: climate change is real, man-made and dangerous.'

So did President Biden's Special Presidential Envoy for Climate, John Kerry, during a speech to graduating students at Boston College warning of the 'crippling consequences' of climate change and that: 'Ninety-seven percent of the world's scientists tell us this is urgent.'

And, of course, Al Gore used a similar message: 'Only an insignificant fraction of scientists deny the global warming crisis. The time for debate is over. The science is settled.'

This claim is widely accepted. Yet the fact that anyone actually believes such total statistical and logical nonsense is a damning indictment of our failing educational system and the asinine gullibility and bias of most of our mainstream media. Let me try and explain where this '97% of scientists' figure came from.

STATISTICAL SMOKE AND MIRRORS?

The main author of the paper which came up with the famous 97% figure was an Australian former web programmer and blogger who later gained a PhD in Philosophy at the School of Psychology, University of Western Australia and then founded what could be seen as a climate alarmist website.

He assembled a group of volunteers and tasked them with 'examining 11,944 climate abstracts from 1991-2011 matching the topics "global climate change" or "global warming"'. Note that the volunteers didn't read the actual scientific papers, they just looked at the abstracts – a summary paragraph or two describing what was in the papers. The volunteers then classed the abstracts into one of seven categories according to their opinions of Anthropogenic Global Warming (AGW):

1. Explicit endorsement of AGW with quantification
2. Explicit endorsement of AGW without quantification
3. Implicit endorsement of AGW
4. No position or Uncertain
5. Implicit rejection of AGW
6. Explicit rejection of AGW without quantification
7. Explicit rejection of AGW with quantification

The reviewers then 'simplified' results into four main categories as follows:

Endorse AGW	3,896	32.6% of abstracts
No AGW position	7,930	66.4% of abstracts
Reject AGW	78	0.7% of abstracts
Uncertain on AGW	40	0.3% of abstracts

So, this gave only 32.6% who, the reviewers concluded, endorsed AGW. This was clearly not quite the stunning super-majority of 97% which the study claimed to have identified.

Now comes the clever bit. Instead of admitting that just 32.6% of papers (actually just abstracts of papers) endorsed AGW, the group decided to remove all the 7,930 abstracts which didn't take a position of AGW. Then, hey presto, magic happened. That left just 4,014 abstracts of which 3,896 (97%) supposedly 'endorsed' AGW.

This was a bit like doing a survey of the voting intentions of 1,000 people. You find that 90 say they'll vote Democrat (U.S.) or Labour (UK) and 10 say they'll vote Republican (U.S.) or Conservative (UK) and the remaining 900 say they're 'undecided'. You then choose to eliminate the 900 'undecideds' and you claim that 90% of voters support Democrats (U.S.) or Labour (UK) and just 10% of voters will vote Republican (U.S.) or Conservative (UK). This is, of course, complete statistical buffoonery as the real percentage of the sampled 1,000 voters who have said they will vote Democrat/Labour is actually just 9% and not 90%.

But that's not the end of the prestidigitation employed to reach that wondrous 97%. The reviewers decided to lump together three categories of abstracts – Explicit endorsement with quantification; Explicit endorsement without quantification and Implicit endorsement. But in the paper claiming 97% support for AGW, the reviewers don't tell us how many papers fitted into each of these three categories. An independent researcher managed to get hold of the original data and claimed to have found out that in 3,896 abstracts which supposedly 'endorsed' AGW, just 64 were in the Explicit endorsement with quantification category; 922 were in the Explicit endorsement without quantification; and the vast majority – 2,910 (out of 3,896) were in the Implicit endorsement of AGW category.[25]

Thus, if this independent researcher's figures are accurate, when you dig down into how the '97% of scientists' figure was actually conjured up, you find that only 986 of 11,944 – that's just 8.2% – of abstracts actually explicitly said they agreed with the theory of man-made global warming. And that's clearly not the kind of figure the apocalypse-threatening warmists would really want to publicise too widely.

So, this '97% of scientists' claim was based on about 11 to 12 (I believe) volunteers, whose scientific credentials have not (as far as I know) been released and all of whom were probably firm AGW believers, each having to look at around 1,000, often quite obtuse, scientific abstracts. During this review, they decided whether they thought the scientific papers (which they hadn't read as they had only looked at the abstracts) explicitly or implicitly supported the

AGW theory. To claim such an approach is 'scientific' is more than ludicrous. To call the '97% of scientists endorse AGW' result garbage could be seen as insulting to garbage.

It is beyond incredible that not a single mainstream-media journalist or editor have had either the ability or the inclination to expose the more than dubious origins of the almost ubiquitous '97% of scientists endorse AGW' claim.

'SCIENTISTS' OR APPROVED SCIENTIFIC ARTICLES?

There are a couple of other issues which further cast doubt on the validity of the '97% of scientists' claim. Firstly, the volunteers were reviewing the abstracts of articles not the opinions of 11,944 individual scientists. In the 11,944 abstracts reviewed, there would be several articles by some scientists. So, those scientists who had written most about climate would have been over-represented.

Moreover, in today's woke Orwellian world, any climate scientist daring to question the officially-approved narrative that CAGW is happening and that it is all the fault of greedy, environment-destroying humans, risks losing their research grants and being deplatformed, cancelled and even fired. So there are rather few scientists who would be particularly enthusiastic about writing articles questioning the CAGW cult and there are few publications that would accept their papers even if they dared to put their heads above the parapet. For example, here's an announcement from the once actually scientific *Scientific American* from April 2021:

SciAm **Scientific American** ✓
@sciam   ···

Scientific American has agreed with major news outlets
worldwide to start using the term "climate emergency"
in its coverage of climate change. Read our statement
about this decision, and the impact we hope it can have
throughout the media landscape.

We Are Living in a Climate Emergency, and We're Going to Say So
It's time to use a term that more than 13,000 scientists agree is needed
🔗 scientificamerican.com

8:00 AM · Apr 12, 2021 · Twitter Web App

Scientific American now claim: 'We are living in a climate emergency, and we're going to say so.' Thus it's hardly likely that the magazine or the other 'major news outlets worldwide' with whom *Scientific American* has agreed to use the term "climate emergency" are going to accept articles by any scientists who suggest that there is no climate emergency. This creates a wonderfully Kafkaesque situation in which articles questioning the CAGW narrative can't get published and then the catastrophists can point to a dearth of articles questioning the CAGW narrative as proof that almost all scientists agree with it.

NOT ALL SCIENTISTS AGREE WITH IMPENDING CLIMATE DISASTER

The mostly climate-alarmist media claim ad nauseam that 97% of scientists believe in catastrophic anthropogenic global warming and that 'the science is settled'. But the media tend not to mention the many thousands of scientists who are appalled at what may be the greatest and costliest scientific blunder in human history.

For example, I doubt many readers will have heard of the letter that 49 former NASA astronauts and scientists sent to NASA expressing their concerns over NASA's apparent obsession with the idea of catastrophic anthropogenic global warming:

March 28, 2012
The Honorable Charles Bolden, Jr.
NASA Administrator
NASA Headquarters
Washington, D.C. 20546-0001

Dear Charlie,
 We, the undersigned, respectfully request that NASA and the Goddard Institute for Space Studies (GISS) refrain from including unproven remarks in public releases and websites. We believe the claims by NASA and GISS, that man-made carbon dioxide is having a catastrophic impact on global climate change are not substantiated, especially when considering thousands of years of

empirical data. With hundreds of well-known climate scientists and tens of thousands of other scientists publicly declaring their disbelief in the catastrophic forecasts, coming particularly from the GISS leadership, it is clear that the science is NOT settled.

The unbridled advocacy of CO2 being the major cause of climate change is unbecoming of NASA's history of making an objective assessment of all available scientific data prior to making decisions or public statements.

As former NASA employees, we feel that NASA's advocacy of an extreme position, prior to a thorough study of the possible overwhelming impact of natural climate drivers is inappropriate. We request that NASA refrain from including unproven and unsupported remarks in its future releases and websites on this subject. At risk is damage to the exemplary reputation of NASA, NASA's current or former scientists and employees, and even the reputation of science itself.

For additional information regarding the science behind our concern, we recommend that you contact Harrison Schmitt or Walter Cunningham, or others they can recommend to you.

Thank you for considering this request.
Sincerely,
(Attached signatures)

There was also the *Manhattan Declaration* which received remarkably little media attention.[26] Over 100 climate specialists from around the world met at a conference centre in New York in March 2008 and endorsed the following:

We, the scientists and researchers in climate and related fields, economists, policymakers, and business leaders, assembled at Times Square, New York City, participating in the 2008 International Conference on Climate Change, Resolving that scientific questions should be evaluated solely by the scientific method; Affirming that global climate has always changed and always will, independent of the actions of humans, and that carbon dioxide (CO_2) is not a pollutant but rather a necessity for all life; Recognising that the causes and extent of recently-observed climatic change are the subject of intense debates in the climate science community and that oft-repeated assertions of a supposed 'consensus' among climate experts are false:

Affirming that attempts by governments to legislate costly regulations on industry and individual citizens to encourage CO_2 emission reduction will slow development while having no appreciable impact on the future trajectory of global climate change. Such policies will markedly diminish future prosperity and so reduce the ability of societies to adapt to inevitable climate change, thereby increasing, not decreasing human suffering;

Noting that warmer weather is generally less harmful to life on Earth than colder: Hereby declare: That current plans to restrict anthropogenic CO_2 emissions are a dangerous misallocation of intellectual capital and resources that should be dedicated to solving humanity's real and serious problems.

That there is no convincing evidence that CO_2 emissions from modern industrial activity has in the past, is now, or will in the future cause catastrophic climate change. That attempts by governments to inflict taxes and costly regulations on industry and individual citizens with the aim of reducing emissions of CO_2 will pointlessly curtail the prosperity of the West and progress of developing nations without affecting climate.

That adaptation as needed is massively more cost-effective than any attempted mitigation, and that a focus on such mitigation will divert the attention and resources of governments away from addressing the real problems of their peoples. That human-caused climate change is not a global crisis.

Now, therefore, we recommend – That world leaders reject the views expressed by the United Nations Intergovernmental Panel on Climate Change as well as popular, but misguided works such as *"An Inconvenient Truth"*. That all taxes, regulations, and other interventions intended to reduce emissions of CO_2 be abandoned forthwith.

Agreed at New York, 4 March 2008

In 2009, 166 scientists wrote an open letter to the U.N. Secretary-General which started off saying:

His Excellency Ban Ki Moon
Secretary-General, United Nations
New York, NY
United States of America
December 8, 2009

Dear Secretary-General,

Climate change science is in a period of 'negative discovery' – the more we learn about this exceptionally complex and rapidly evolving field the more we realize how little we know. Truly, the science is NOT settled.

Therefore, there is no sound reason to impose expensive and restrictive public policy decisions on the peoples of the Earth without first providing convincing evidence that human activities are causing dangerous climate change beyond that resulting from natural causes. Before any precipitate action is taken, we must have solid observational data demonstrating that recent changes in climate differ substantially from changes observed in the past and are well in excess of normal variations caused by solar cycles, ocean currents, changes in the Earth's orbital parameters and other natural phenomena.

We the undersigned, being qualified in climate-related scientific disciplines, challenge the UNFCCC and supporters of the United Nations Climate Change Conference to produce convincing

OBSERVATIONAL EVIDENCE for their claims of dangerous human-caused global warming and other changes in climate. Projections of possible future scenarios from unproven computer models of climate are not acceptable substitutes for real world data obtained through unbiased and rigorous scientific investigation.

And in 2009, an organisation called the Cato Institute took out a full-page newspaper ad which attacked President Barack Obama's convictions about global warming. The ad cites then-President-elect Obama's November 19 statement: "Few challenges facing America and the world are more urgent than combating climate change. The science is beyond dispute and the facts are clear."

"With all due respect, Mr. President, that is not true," the ad states in bold letters. Below that is a statement they say was signed off on by more than 100 named scientists.

"We, the undersigned scientists, maintain that the case for alarm regarding climate change is grossly overstated. Surface temperature changes over the past century have been episodic and modest and there has been no net global warming for over a decade now. After controlling for population growth and property values, there has been no increase in damages from severe weather-related events. The computer models forecasting rapid temperature change abjectly fail to explain recent climate behavior. Mr. President, your characterization of the scientific facts regarding climate change and the degree of certainty informing the scientific debate is simply incorrect."

PART 4

What's really happening

Although originally thought that the CO_2 data might be considered as proof of its causal role in global warming, it is now widely considered that CO_2 lags temperature change,' From an article in *Periodicals of Engineering and Natural Sciences* 2 August 2019

CHAPTER 10

CO2 and climate

Given the utter panic from the climate catastrophists and sycophantic, scientifically-ignorant media about the supposed dangers of rising CO2 levels, it might be worth putting the amounts of CO2 in our atmosphere into context. CO2 is what is called a 'trace gas'. There is so little CO2 in our atmosphere that it has to be measured in 'parts per million' (ppm). Most of our atmosphere – 99% – consists of nitrogen (78%) and oxygen (21%). Then there are the trace gases. The most common of these is argon (0.9%). Then comes CO2 (0.04%) and almost negligible quantities of neon, helium, methane and krypton (Figure 1).[27]

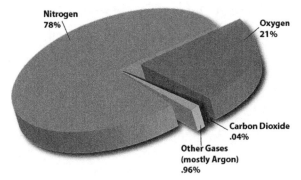

Figure 1 – Composition of the Earth's atmosphere (From University Corporation for Atmospheric Research)

To try to illustrate how little CO_2 there actually is in the atmosphere, we could take two well-known sports stadiums – the Michigan Stadium in the U.S. with a capacity of 107,600 and Wembley Stadium in Britain with a capacity of 90,000. If the total capacity of each stadium represented the atmosphere, then the pre-industrial level of CO_2 of about 280 ppm would represent just 30 seats in the 107,600-seat Michigan Stadium and a mere 25 seats in the 90,000-seat Wembley Stadium. Measurements have shown that CO_2 has risen from 280 ppm to about 417 ppm in the last 140 years. That is a significant rise of 49%. But as CO_2 is just a trace gas, the increase would mean adding just an extra 15 seats in the Michigan Stadium over a period of 140 years – about one seat every 10 years – and only 12 seats at Wembley over 140 years. Yet we are instructed by our political, scientific and media elites to believe that this tiny amount of increased trace gas as part of our atmosphere – from 0.028% to 0.042% – will cause catastrophic changes in our climate and the extinction of the human race.

We know that the two most common gases in our atmosphere – nitrogen (78%) and oxygen (21%) – are not 'greenhouse gases'. That means they don't trap heat in the atmosphere making the Earth warmer. So, to understand how greenhouse gases may affect the Earth's climate we need to look at the relative quantities of the main greenhouse gases. If you go to Google images and look for a pie chart displaying the amount of each greenhouse gas, you'll get something like this (Figure 2).

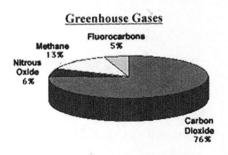

This graph shows the distribution of GHG in Earth's atmosphere. Carbon Dioxide is clearly the majority.
www.abcnews.com/sections/us/global106.html

Figure 2 – The main greenhouse gases?

This used to appear on the ABC News website, but has since been taken down. However, there's a more than small problem with this and many similar representations. They all invariably suggest that CO_2 is the main greenhouse gas. But the main greenhouse gas is actually water vapour. In fact, water vapour accounts for at least 90% of the Earth's greenhouse gases. CO_2 only makes up around 6% of greenhouse gases. Methane and others constitute the remaining 4%. You can find confirmation of water vapour being the main greenhouse gas deep in the bowels of the text of the 2007 report from the Intergovernmental Panel on Climate Change (IPCC): 'Water vapour is the most abundant and important greenhouse gas in the atmosphere.' The IPCC report goes on to state: 'However, human activities have only a small direct influence on the amount of atmospheric water vapour.'

In spite of water vapour being by far the most abundant greenhouse gas, you seldom, if ever, hear the climate catastrophists mentioning it and demanding we reduce it. This is probably because, as the IPCC explains: 'Human activities have only a small direct influence on the amount of atmospheric water vapour.'

Perhaps it's slightly amusing that many newspaper and magazine articles about our impending extinction due to CO_2-driven climate change illustrate their panic and disaster stories with pictures of power-station cooling towers pouring out supposed atmospheric pollution:

In fact, what is pouring out of these cooling towers is steam – water vapour – the Earth's most abundant greenhouse gas.

Water vapour, CO_2 and methane all have different levels of heat insulation. But with water vapour making up such a large percentage of greenhouse gases, it should be clear that even a small percentage increase in water vapour will have a much greater effect on the Earth's temperature than a much larger percentage increase in CO_2 or methane.

We're forever being bombarded with charts supposedly proving that increasing atmospheric CO2 is causing temperature increases (Figure 3).

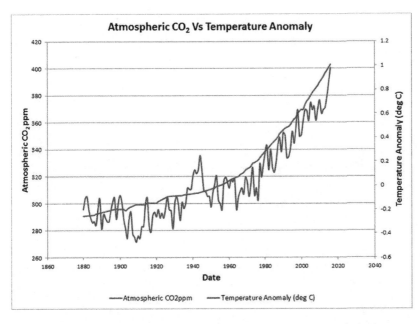

Figure 3 – Proof that increasing CO2 and temperatures are linked?

But in spite of the fact that water vapour constitutes possibly 90% of greenhouse gases, the climate catastrophists never seem to mention that water vapour has also been increasing in the lower atmosphere (section A on Figure 4) and in the upper atmosphere (section B on Figure 4).[28]

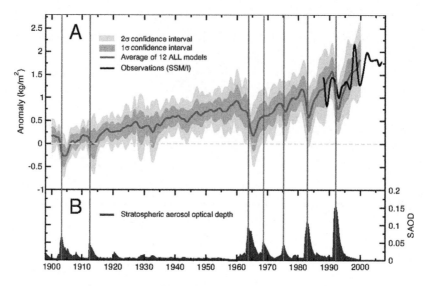

Figure 4 – The main greenhouse gas – water vapour – has been increasing

As the Earth warms, more water vapour is released from the oceans. As water vapour is the main greenhouse gas, increasing water vapour in the atmosphere will trap more heat thus increasing the warming. So you could easily redraw the CO2 and temperature chart (Figure 3 above) substituting rising CO2 with rising water vapour and use that to prove that the main greenhouse gas, water vapour, is driving global warming. Water vapour, which constitutes up to 90% of greenhouse gases, may be acting as a forcer of warming in exactly the way that the CO2-catastrophists claim CO2 is increasing warming. In fact, as there's about fifteen times as much water vapour in the atmosphere than CO2, if there is a greenhouse effect, it's more likely that increasing water vapour is the main cause.

A climate rationalist might be tempted to wonder why the climate alarmists apparently never consider that this rise in the world's most abundant greenhouse gas is possibly the obvious main cause of increasing global temperatures.

CARTS AND HORSES

One of the key diagrams used by Al Gore in his Nobel-Prize-winning film *An Inconvenient Truth* was a chart made in 1999 of the Earth's temperatures and atmospheric CO_2 concentration going back about 400,000 years (Figure 5). This chart was based on analysis of ice cores from the Russian Vostok station in Antarctica.

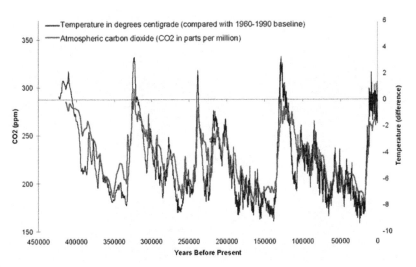

Figure 5 – Temperature and CO_2

The line which starts higher on your left (the blue line if you're reading an ebook) is temperature and the other (lower) line (red line in the ebook) is CO_2. Looking at this chart, it's easy to see how Gore and various climate catastrophists concluded that this chart shows a clear relationship between temperature and CO_2 levels with CO_2 driving temperature changes. Thus it was reasonable to postulate that the rapidly-rising CO_2 levels to record highs following the West's industrialisation could lead to record high global temperatures.

But further analysis done for a paper published in 2019, thirteen years after Al Gore's film really set the lucrative CAGW bandwagon rolling, produced a very different picture (Figure 6).

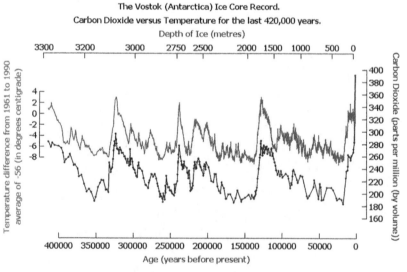

Figure 6 – Further analysis of the Vostok ice cores

Temperature is the upper line and the scale on your left (the red line in an ebook). Atmospheric CO_2 concentration is the lower line and scale on your right (blue line in an ebook).

The importance of this new chart can be found in a 2 August 2019 paper published in the *Periodicals of Engineering and Natural Sciences*.[29] The authors conducted detailed analyses of the Vostok ice cores and divided them into four time periods. They found that in three of the four time periods: 'CO2 lags temperature.' The data from the fourth period wasn't so clear. However, the conclusion of this 2019 study was incredibly important: 'Although originally thought that the CO2 data might be considered as proof of its causal role in global warming, it is now widely considered that CO2 lags temperature change and its lower rate of solution in and release from sea water is more likely the cause of the relationship.'

The Earth's atmosphere contains about 720 billion tons (gigatons) of CO2 (some sources say 730 gigatons and NASA says 750 gigatons) and the oceans around 37,400 gigatons (some sources say 38,000 gigatons). When sea water warms, it releases CO2 into the atmosphere. When sea water cools, it absorbs more CO2 from the atmosphere. Instead of CO2 levels driving temperature changes, the authors are saying that CO2 levels are being driven by temperature changes. So when the Earth warms, atmospheric CO2 levels increase as more CO2 is released from the warming oceans into the atmosphere. Then when the Earth cools, CO2 levels in the atmosphere fall as the cooling oceans absorb more atmospheric CO2. Moreover, there is a lag of several hundred years between the Earth warming/cooling and the level of atmospheric CO2 rising/falling as it takes time for atmospheric warming/cooling to warm/cool the oceans.

If one were to caricature the situation, Gore and his climate catastrophe disciples saw a horse and a cart moving along a road closely together and concluded that the cart was pushing the horse. But more recent analysis has indicated that it is in fact the horse which is pulling the cart.

Of course, this paper may be wrong. But it perhaps better explains changes in our climate than the CAGW theory. For example, it's clear from the chart that climate change is cyclical – the Earth warms and cools in regular cycles. We can also see this in more recent temperature reconstructions (Figure 7).

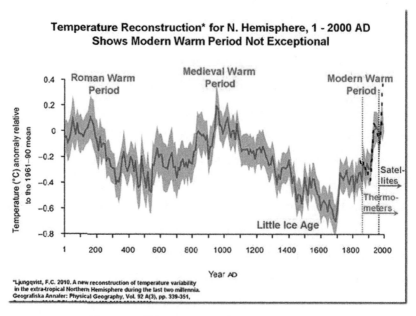

Figure 7 – Temperature cycles over 2,000 years

But if the CAGW theory of increasing atmospheric CO_2 driving rising temperatures were true, then we wouldn't have these warming and cooling cycles. Instead, rising CO_2 would drive rising temperatures which would cause the oceans to release more CO_2 leading to more rising temperatures and so on until the Earth burned up. As this hasn't happened, this suggests that something other than atmospheric CO_2 levels is causing the cyclical changes in the Earth's temperature. The climate catastrophists could argue that with CO_2 levels now almost 50% higher than they have been for the last 400,000 or more years, we're in a completely new situation. But this would ignore the fact that CO_2 levels have been much higher in the past and yet the Earth's temperature didn't shoot up and destroy all life (Figure 8).[30]

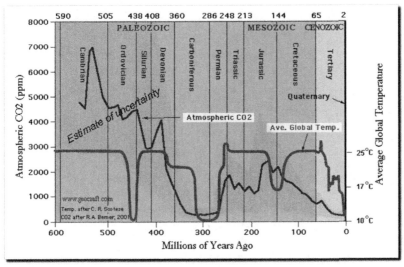

Figure 8 – Atmospheric CO_2 and temperature over 600 million years

The upper line and the scale on your left indicate atmospheric CO_2 levels and the lower line and the scale on your right are the Earth's temperature. In the past, between 600 and 450 million years ago, when atmospheric CO_2 levels were above 3,000 ppm, the Earth's temperature was only around 25°C (compared to about 13.9°C today). Then in the Carboniferous and Permian periods, between 360 and 250 million years ago, both CO_2 and temperature fell to record low levels. Both started climbing again till around 140 million years ago. Then CO_2 started dropping towards the pre-industrial level of around 280 ppm, while global temperature remained high for another 80 million years till the start of the Tertiary Period. In fact, according to generally accepted paleoclimatic reconstructions, both atmospheric CO_2 levels and the Earth's temperature are now close to record low levels – for much of the Earth's history, temperatures have been higher than they are today (Figure 9).[31]

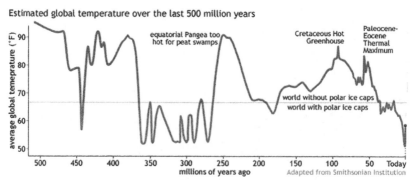

Figure 9 – Earth's land temperatures over 500 million years

The conclusion that temperature changes drive changes in atmospheric CO_2 levels (instead of the climate catastrophists' claims that CO2 drives temperature) is so explosive that you would have expected it to be reported in every news media throughout the world. If it is an accurate interpretation of the science, then it is telling us that there's probably no need to limit human CO2 emissions, no need to decarbonise our economies, no need to destroy our key industries, no need to throw millions out of work, and no need to tax fossil fuels out of existence. Yet, as far as I am aware, not a single mainstream media outlet chose to report this.

Unfortunately, it seems that we're too far down the road of the catastrophic anthropogenic global warming delusion to turn back or even dare question its scientific basis. There are so many academic and political careers and reputations dependent on CAGW, so many lucrative research grants, so many school courses on CAGW, so many millions of schoolchildren who have been indoctrinated into the CAGW cult, so many 20,000- to 30,000-attendee international conferences on CAGW, so many hundreds of thousands of activists convinced evil humans are destroying their planet that, however strong the growing body of evidence that we're probably committing the greatest scientific, economic and social blunder in human history, we're trapped into continuing with our self-flagellating, narcissistic self-harm in pursuit of a goal – reducing CO2 emissions – which is rather pointless and which will have little to no influence on the cyclical changes in the Earth's climate.

Seemingly we've learnt nothing since Charles Mackay's 1841 book – *Extraordinary Popular Delusions and the Madness of Crowds*:

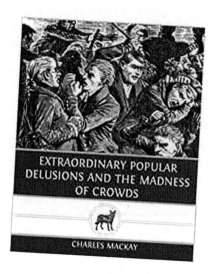

Mackay covers the biggest financial scandals in history – the Mississippi Scheme, the South Sea Bubble and Tulipmania. But he also looks at the greatest charlatans who have caused waves of public hysteria. There were, for example, the astrologers in 16th century London who calculated that the Thames would rise and swallow all of London on February 1st 1524. After their prophecy did not, of course, come true, they saved their necks by arguing that they made a slight mistake in their calculations which made them err by 100 years. That gave them plenty of time to carry on earning a good living from their soothsaying without any risk of being shown up as mountebanks. Their story might sound familiar to readers who have seen how many times the climate alarmists have warned us of the melting of the Arctic sea ice, the flooding of our coastal cities, the destruction of our agriculture and all the other woes that should have already come from CAGW and most definitely, if you believe the catastrophists, will afflict us in the future.

Likewise the book tells the story of medieval sermonizers and fanatics who saw a sign of the coming world doom in every phenomenon of nature. Again, some readers might see some similarity with the ever more febrile antics of today's climate catastrophists. But in spite of the many predictions of disaster, the world kept turning and continues to do so. No doubt there will always be astrologers and suchlike (the equivalent of some modern-day "scientists") who will earn a good living and get lots of free publicity by telling us that we are all doomed if we do not act.

EARTH'S TEMPERATURE SHOOTS UP FROM 12.8°C TO 13.9°C. PANIC!

The type of charts used by the climate catastrophists to sow panic and fear and thus our obedience to their ever more oppressive curtailment of our freedoms in order to save the planet are usually something like Figure 10.

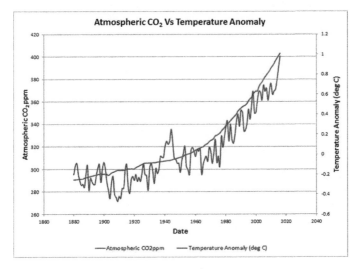

Figure 10 – CO2 and temperature

The upward curving line is atmospheric CO_2 rising from just under 300 parts per million (ppm) to just above 400 ppm – actually 417 ppm by April 2021. The fluctuating line is global temperature. It seems at first sight as if these two lines are rising at very similar rates supposedly confirming a very tight relationship between atmospheric CO_2 and temperature. But we have to be careful as this chart and many like it could be very misleading.

The scale on the left shows that CO_2 has risen by about 49% since 1880. But the scale on the right – the scale for temperature – is almost always expressed as an 'anomaly' – a variation from an average. The average can be the 20th Century or the years 1880 to 2000 or whatever the chartist chooses. But it's very difficult to find a CO_2 vs temperature chart which actually tells you what that average temperature is in degrees. That could lead a climate rationalist to wonder why this information is almost never mentioned.

In fact, over the last 140 years since 1880, global temperatures have probably risen by just over 1°C from around 12.8°C (55.04°F) to around 13.9°C (57.02°F) – about 8% in 140 years. That's an increase of only 0.8°C per century – an increase of about 6% every 100 years. Though the Intergovernmental Panel on Climate Change puts the increase in global mean surface temperature over the last 100 years significantly lower at just 0.3°C to 0.6°C. However, even if we take the higher estimated 0.8°C suggested by some experts, a 49% increase in atmospheric Co_2 has occurred while temperatures have risen by just 8%.

Had the two scales on the chart both been in percentages against a historic average or a base year, you'd see that, while CO_2 was shooting up 49% in 140 years, temperatures were fairly flat merely increasing by a mere 8%. So, it wouldn't look like there was much of a relationship at all between CO2 levels and temperature. But it would hardly fit the catastrophists' agenda of spreading the maximum amount of fear and alarm if they were to rush onto the media shouting that global temperatures had risen from 12.8°C to 13.9°C over the last 140 years – an almost imperceptible 0.008°C a year.

In fact, if that was their message, the media probably would have yawned and ignored them. So, instead we get highly misleading charts, which use dodgy scales to hugely exaggerate the temperature rise to make it fit with the rise in CO2 levels. Then, on the basis of these dodgy charts we're bombarded with doom-mongering predictions of melting ice caps, flooded cities, horrific droughts, mass starvation and soaring temperatures for which there is absolutely no factual basis.

And just to show the games that can be played using charts, here are three charts – atmospheric CO2 levels at the top, global life expectancy on your left and global literacy levels on your right. (Figure 11).

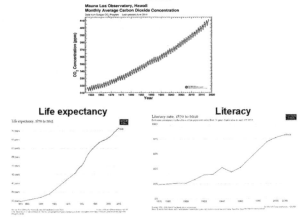

Figure 11 – CO2 vs Life Expectancy vs Literacy

You will see that there is fairly good correlation between rising CO_2 levels and rising life expectancy and increasing literacy. However, I'm not for a moment suggesting that breathing in more CO_2 helps you live longer or that more CO_2 helps you become better at reading. I'm merely trying to show that, although correlations may look convincing if you make charts with similar scales and similar trends, correlation does not always prove causation. So, we should be very careful when catastrophists come waving their charts supposedly 'proving' that rising CO_2 is the cause of rising global temperatures just because the two seem to be following similar trends. And we should be especially careful when the scales on the alarmists' charts are adjusted to make it look like CO_2 and temperatures have risen by similar amounts when CO_2 levels have risen by 49% and temperatures have only risen by, at most, 8% and (according to the IPCC) possibly even less than that.

CO2 IS GOOD FOR YOU

In 2007, the U.S. state of Massachusetts brought a case against the U.S. Environmental Protection Agency (EPA) forcing the EPA to accept that CO_2 was a 'pollutant' – a toxic gas – which the EPA had a duty to regulate under the Clean Air Act.[32] If implemented by politicians, this meant that the EPA could be forced to set limits on how much CO_2 would be permitted to be emitted by industry, transport, hospitals – in fact from every aspect of life.

The climate catastrophists constantly claim that rising CO_2 is causing climate change which will devastate agriculture and lead to mass starvation. For example: 'In the long list of potential problems from global warming, the risks to world agriculture stand out as among the most important.'[33] And the Executive Director of Oxfam International opined: 'Climate change is the biggest threat to our chances of winning the fight against hunger.'[34] Given that the population of Africa doubles every 21 to 22 years and is projected to rise from about 1.2 billion in 2021 to over 3 billion by 2060 and over 4 billion by the end of this century, perhaps the Executive Director of Oxfam International and her colleagues at Oxfam should worry less about supposed climate change and a bit more about the real 'biggest threat to our chances of winning the fight against hunger'?

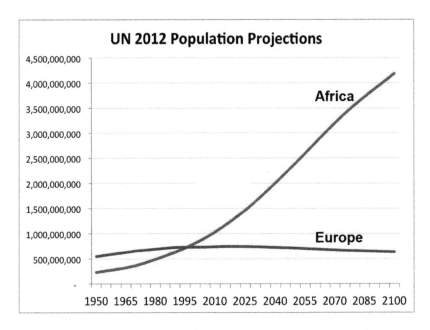

As for the claim by the alarmists that rising CO2 will damage world agriculture and devastate food production, in common with so many other hyperbolic, shroud-waving pronouncements by the CAGW aficionados, it's probable that the exact opposite is true.

About 100 years ago, the formerly serious magazine *Scientific American* published an article on 27 November 1920 extolling the benefits for plant growth of air that was enriched with CO_2:

The article informed us that: 'Whereas atmospheric air at present is relatively poor in carbonic acid, of which it contains only about 0.03 per cent (300 ppm), at an early period in the development of our planet, when this was covered with the luxuriant forests our coal deposits are derived from, it comprised incomparably greater quantities of this gas.' The article went on to say: 'This fact suggested the idea of heightening the fertility of the soil by increasing its carbonic acid content and thus producing conditions resembling those of antediluvian ages.'

More recently, scientists have been (possibly reluctantly?) recognising that rising CO2 is not causing the famine, starvation and ruination that so many so enthusiastically predicted. Instead, rising CO2 is leading to a 'greening' of the Earth:

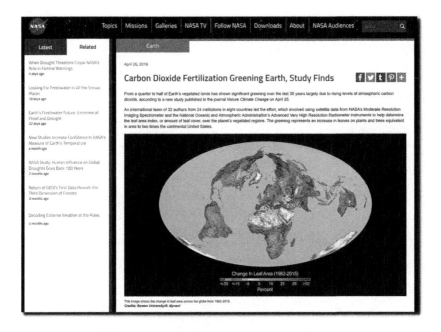

One recent report noted that:

'Near daily observations since the early 1980s from NASA and NOAA satellites reveal vast expanses of the Earth's vegetated lands from the Arctic to the temperate latitudes exhibiting vigorous growing tendencies. . . . Notably, the NASA MODIS sensors observed pronounced greening during the 21st century in the most populous and developing countries, China and India. Even regions far, far removed from human reach have not escaped global warming and greening. Svalbard in the high-arctic, for example, has seen a 30% increase in greenness.'[35]

Many other studies have confirmed that rising atmospheric CO_2 is contributing to the Earth's greening, for example: 'We show a persistent and widespread increase of growing season integrated greening over 25% to 50% of the global vegetated area, whereas less than 4% of the globe shows browning.'[36]

Along with improved farming methods, the Earth's greening is contributing to a significant rise in food production. This is a fact that extinctionists don't seem to have considered as they scream and howl about rising CO_2 leading to desertification and starvation. Not only is increasing CO_2 leading to improved plant growth, but many food producers using greenhouses increase the levels of CO_2 by installing CO_2 generators in their greenhouses:

Typically, these CO_2 generators raise atmospheric CO_2 levels in greenhouses to between 1,000 ppm and 1,500 ppm and lead to a

30% to 40% increase in crop yields. Whereas those extinctionists, who have hair, are tearing it out at the thought of atmospheric CO_2 rising above the current level of just over 417 ppm (in April 2021), it has been suggested that, if CO_2 concentration was to reach 600 ppm, the yield of the top ten food crops would increase by more than a third.[37] One expert, a Nobel laureate, has even proposed that the ideal atmospheric CO_2 level might be somewhere around 1,000 ppm – more than twice today's level.

On its website, in a section called 'The Causes of Climate Change', a NASA scientist writes: 'Some laboratory experiments suggest that elevated CO_2 levels can increase plant growth.' But this highly misleading. It's not just 'some laboratory experiments' which 'suggest that elevated CO_2 can increase plant growth'. We have known for at least 100 years that increasing CO_2 levels do improve plant growth. And we know that thousands, or even tens of thousands, of food producers around the world put CO_2 generators in their greenhouses to achieve a 30% to 40% increase in crop yields. Yet NASA, who should be providing us with objective scientific information, are so desperate to discredit any claims that rising CO_2 may be not be quite as poisonous and catastrophic as the alarmists always claim, is shamelessly pumping out what can only be described as 'anti-CO_2 propaganda' in order to cast doubt on any possible benefits of increased atmospheric CO_2. After all, ordinary people might stop panicking about increasing CO_2 levels if they realised that rising CO_2 might actually have some benefits for mankind. NASA go on to try to further discredit the possible benefits of increasing CO_2 on plant growth by suggesting: 'although rising CO_2 can stimulate plant growth, research has shown that it can also reduce the nutritional value of most crops.'

Moreover, while hectoring us about the need to reduce atmospheric CO2, the climate alarmists tend not to mention that, were the atmospheric CO2 level ever to fall towards 150 ppm, that would probably lead to catastrophic crop failures and the famines and starvation which the climate catastrophists claim will come from rising CO2. Hopefully the climate alarmists will take this into account as they lobby our governments for the subsidising and building of more 'Direct Air Capture' machines to scrub CO2 out of the atmosphere in what has been estimated to become a $100 billion market by 2030.[38] It would be more than unfortunate if the crazed catastrophists killed us all by causing low atmospheric CO2 through sucking CO2 out of the atmosphere while trying to save us from high atmospheric CO2.

CHAPTER 11

What about the sun?

SETTLED SCIENCE?

Climate catastrophists constantly claim that 'the science is settled' and that anyone questioning whether CAGW is happening is like a member of the Flat Earth Society. For example, when laying out a series of measures aimed at curbing climate change, including limits on emissions from power plants, U.S. President Barack Obama said he would not waste time debating with those who denied CAGW was happening: 'We don't have time for a meeting of the Flat Earth Society.' And he warned: 'Sticking your head in the sand might make you feel safer but it's not going to protect you from the coming storm.'

But when you look at the climate alarmists' bible – the reports from the Intergovernmental Panel on Climate Change (IPCC) – you don't find the degree of certainty expressed by people who possibly have more scientific knowledge than Mr Obama. In the Scientific Assessment of the first IPCC report in 1990 there appeared to be some degree of doubt about whether the warming of the previous

100 years had been caused by increasing atmospheric CO_2 levels due to the burning of fossil fuels or was a result of natural variations in climate which have nothing to do with human activities:

> There are many uncertainties in our predictions particularly with regard to the timing, magnitude and regional patterns of climate change due to our incomplete understanding. Global mean surface air temperature has increased by 0.3°C to 0.6°C over the last 100 years. The size of this warming is broadly consistent with predictions of climate change models, but it is also of the same magnitude as natural climate variability. Thus the observed increase could be largely due to this natural variability; alternatively this variability and other human factors could have offset a still larger human-induced greenhouse warming.[39]

MAYBE THE SUN MIGHT PLAY A PART?

It might seem odd to a climate realist that climate catastrophists are absolutely convinced that increasing atmospheric CO_2 is the main driver – 'forcer' – of global warming when the sun makes up 99.85% of the mass of our solar system and the sun supplies about 99.98% of the energy which drives our climate.

Of course, the theory of CAGW is pleasingly simple and easy to communicate. It goes something like this: CO_2 has been relatively stable for at least the last 400,000 years; since industrialisation CO_2 has increased by a huge 49% mainly due to humans burning fossil fuels and changing land use; CO2 is a greenhouse gas; while atmospheric CO2 has increased, the Earth's temperature has also risen; therefore, although there will always be natural variations in the Earth's climate, it is clear that increasing CO2 from human activities must be the main forcer for the increase in the Earth's temperature.

However, there are competing theories about our planet's warming. One of these, which is possibly slightly more complicated than the CO2-driven warming and which is hardly ever mentioned in the media, is that it might be the sun's activity which is driving the Earth's changing temperature. There are hundreds of scientific articles giving various, often complex and sometimes largely incomprehensible to the layman (and laywoman), explanations of how the sun might be the main cause of the last 140 years' increase in global temperatures of about 1.1°C. To simplify these to a degree that would probably horrify most scientists, one could say that it is believed that there are two main ways the sun is affecting the Earth's climate – variations in solar activity and variations in the orbit and tilt of the Earth around the sun. These are explained in an IPCC report:

What factors can change climate? Any factor which alters the radiation received from the Sun or lost to space, or which alters the redistribution of energy within the atmosphere, and between the atmosphere, land and ocean, will affect climate. The Sun's output of energy is known to change by small amounts over an 11-year cycle, and variations over longer periods may occur. On time-scales of tens to thousands of years, slow variations in the Earth's orbit have led to changes in the seasonal and latitudinal distribution of solar radiation; these changes have played an important part in controlling the variations of past climate.

So, the IPCC is giving us two possible ways the sun might be driving the Earth's climate – variations in solar energy reaching the Earth both over the 11-year solar cycle and over medium periods (hundreds of years) and and variations in solar energy over longer periods (hundreds of thousands of years) through changes in the Earth's orbit.

VARIATIONS IN SOLAR ACTIVITY

In the early 19th Century, an astronomer called William Herschel noticed a correlation between the number of sunspots and wheat prices. During periods when there were more sunspots, wheat prices tended to be lower. Conversely, the absence of sunspots coincided with high wheat prices. He read his paper at a Royal Society meeting in London and, as so often happens in science when a breakthrough in understanding is made which demolishes previous theories, he was reportedly 'heartily ridiculed' by the members.[40]

More recent research has found that over hundreds of years there appears to be a strong correlation between periods of low sunspot activity and lower temperatures and periods of high sunspot activity and warmer temperatures. For example, a period which is called the 'Maunder Minimum', named after astronomers

Edward and Annie Maunder, coincided with the Little Ice Age and the Dalton Minimum occurred at a time when global temperatures are believed to have fallen significantly below average. Moreover, rising sunspot numbers appear to match the rising temperatures since around 1900 in what has been called the 'Modern Maximum' (Figure 1).

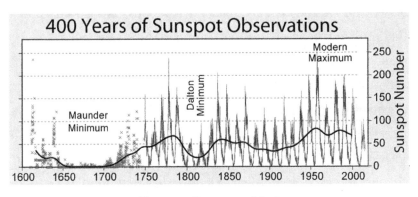

Figure 1 – Sunspot activity[41]

In the 20th Century, scientists were starting to link high temperatures to high levels of sunspot activity:

> ### The New York Times
>
> THURSDAY, JULY 2, 1931
>
> "Hottest Summer in four thousand years" may be the headline of a meteorological report of the future, thanks to the studies of DOUG-LASS and ANTEVS. Already scientists are able to throw light on past climates and the correspondence of weather with fluctuations in the sun's heat. That there is some relation between sun spots and our weather has long been suspected by meteorologists. Now they are certain. The long-range weather-forecaster has the means of correlating his records, extending back little more than a century, with those that

There are several theories about how variations in solar activity may be affecting the climate. Here I'll just (mainly for my own sake) deal with one of the most straightforward.

Satellite measurements since 1979 have shown that the number of sunspots correlate with the intensity of solar radiation reaching the Earth. Most estimates of this variation since 1979 put it at between 0.1% and 0.2%. Over longer periods, as Figure 1 shows, the variation between sunspot numbers has been much greater than it has been since 1979. But if we just take the 0.1% to 0.2% variation in solar activity since 1979, this is so small that climate alarmists have contemptuously dismissed it as being negligible in terms of influencing the climate. Suggesting that the variation in solar radiation might be the real cause of global temperature changes has even been called 'scientifically irresponsible.'

But a little simple arithmetic might suggest that dismissing this 0.1% to 0.2% variation in solar radiation as having a negligible effect on temperatures may not be quite as ridiculous as the CO_2-catastrophists like to claim. The Fourth IPCC Assessment Report in 2007 explains that the solar radiation reaching the Earth is estimated at around 1,368 watts per square metre (W/m^2). Other experts have used the figure of 1,361.5 (W/m^2). As with almost everything concerning the complex multifaceted thermodynamic system that is the Earth's climate, it's difficult to find any two experts who agree about anything – except, of course, for the catastrophists who are all convinced we're doomed, doomed, doomed.

Here we'll use the lower figure to be on the safe side. As there are two hemispheres and day and night, some scientists express this solar energy as an average of 340 W/m² (¼ of 1,361.5). The warming impact of the total CO_2 in the atmosphere has been estimated to be about 2 W/m².[42] Of this around 5% of the CO_2 comes from human activities. So, human activities might be responsible for adding 0.1 W/m² (5% of 2 W/m²) to the Earth's warming. But the variation in solar radiation from variations in sunspot activity can add anywhere between 0.3 W/m² to 0.6 W/m². That's three to six times the warming that catastrophists claim is caused by human emissions of CO_2. These figures may not be correct. But they do suggest that the theory of the sun's activity being the main driver of climate changes should not be so sneeringly rejected by those pushing the 'rising-anthropogenic-CO_2-will-kill-us-all' message.

Another line catastrophists often take when trying to dismiss any suggestion that solar activity, and not CO_2, might be the main driver of temperature changes is that:

'The current scientific consensus, most specifically that of the IPCC, is that solar variations only play a marginal role in driving global climate change since the measured magnitude of recent solar variation is much smaller than the forcing due to greenhouse gases.' But the simple arithmetic above suggests this may not be true. Moreover, the IPCC writes 'greenhouse gases' and not 'CO_2'. As water vapour makes up around 90% of greenhouse gases, it's far from clear whether the IPCC believes that variations in solar activity do actually have a smaller forcing effect than CO_2 on its own or not.

In 1951, a professor of meteorology at the Massachusetts Institute of Technology predicted 'a colder, wetter 15 or 20 years' based on his observations of declining sunspot activity:

The Daily Pantagraph
CENTRAL ILLINOIS' HOME NEWSPAPER SINCE 1846

MONDAY, MAY 7, 1951.

Professor Predicts Colder Cycle Ahead Forecast Based On History Of Sunspots

BOSTON — (AP) — There's a colder, wetter 15 or 20 years in your future.

That is, if you are a North American, a European or an Asiatic and if you don't live in certain special places.

Hurd C. Willett, professor of meteorology at the Massachusetts Institute of Technology has studied a couple of hundred years of sunspot cycles and weather. Using a weather yardstick constructed of what's happened in the past, he has laid it upon the future and has come up with a long range forecast.

Among other things, he says glaciers will advance.

Professor Willett's "extrapolation of sunspot-climate relationships" appears in the American Meteorological Society's Journal of Meteorology.

Sure enough, the Little Cooling of the 1960s and 1970s, when colder weather led climatologists to worry about the onset of a new Ice Age, followed. And by 1994, some scientists were proposing that sunspot activity, and not greenhouse gases, were the main drivers of the global warming that had started again after the 1960s and 1970s Little Cooling:

The Canberra Times

FRIDAY, APRIL 8, 1994

Sunspots linked to global warming

Gases not dominant factor

LONDON: Sunspots, rather than "greenhouse" gases from the burning of fossil fuels, may be responsible for the rise in global temperatures in the past 200 years, it was claimed on Wednesday.

Astronomers at Armagh Observatory in Northern Ireland have studied meteorological records going back to 1795, which point to a strong link between air temperatures on Earth and solar activity.

Dr John Butler, who presented the results at the European and National Astronomy Meeting in Edinburgh, said. "It looks as though carbon dioxide [the principal greenhouse gas] has not been the most dominant factor in global warming for the past 200 years."

The new results are bound to fuel political controversy. The right-wing think-tank, the Institute of Economic Affairs, published a pamphlet recently questioning scientific predictions about a link between

rising concentrations of greenhouse gases in the atmosphere and increases in global temperatures. The institute has an explicit economic agenda, urging that governments should take no action to tackle climate change and in particular arguing against the introduction of carbon taxes to decrease the consumption of fossil fuels.

However. Dr Butler said, "Carbon dioxide may well become dominant in future."

His results reinforce claims made a few years ago by two Danish meteorologists who found a correlation between the length of a sunspot cycle and temperatures on Earth.

The Armagh observations contain one local irony. According to Dr Butler, they show that "global

warming has taken 10 years longer to reach Northern Ireland than Central Europe".

He put this down to the proximity of the Atlantic Ocean and the well-known effect that the oceans take longer to heat up land or air. Sunspots are dark patches of gas which are slightly cooler than their surroundings on the surface of the sun.

It is not the number of sunspots which affects the Earth's climate, according to Dr Butler, but the length of the sunspot cycle. This averages about 11 years, but periods when the cycle becomes shorter correspond to greater solar activity and greater energy output.

Dr Butler pointed out that during the past 20 years, the solar cycle has been abnormally short

(about 9.6 years) and the Earth's weather abnormally warm.

On the other hand, a period in the late 17th century known as "The Little Ice Age" when the Thames froze in winter, corresponded with an abnormally long solar cycle, when sunspots virtually stopped for about 60 years.

The Armagh observations are not quite the world's longest continuous series of temperature measurements. Kew has records back to the 1770s.

However, Kew's ancient records are not comparable with more recent ones because of the growth of London. Cities generate their own micro-climate, which is usually a degree or so warmer than the surrounding countryside.

Since the population of Armagh has not mushroomed in the same way as London during the period of the observations, there is a greater consistency in those records.
— The Independent

However, the theory of solar activity being the main driver of the Earth's temperature seemed to fall apart when the level of solar radiation from sunspot activity began to drop around the year 2000 while global temperatures apparently continued relentlessly increasing (Figure 2).[43]

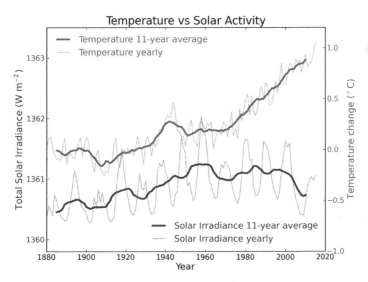

Figure 2 – Temperature vs solar irradiance

Temperature change is the upper (red in the ebook) line and the scale on your right. Solar irradiance is the lower (blue in the ebook) line and scale on your left.

The temperature line used here is the most commonly-used one and is the one which tells us (possibly implausibly?) that the scorching 1920s and 1930s, when thousands died from the heat and scientists predicted melting ice caps and flooded coastal cities, were colder than the Little Cooling of the 1960s and 1970s when scientists were predicting a new Ice Age. As I have hopefully shown (Chapter 9 – Making 'facts' fit the theory), when comparing this temperature chart to newspaper and magazine articles over the last 140 years, this temperature line makes no sense.

Moreover, we know that there was a 12-year pause in the Earth's rising temperature between 2002 and 2014. This pause was even reported by the embarrassingly climate-catastrophist BBC (British Broadcasting Corporation) which continually assures us that 'the science is settled' and that rising CO2 is driving ever-rising global temperature:

But when you look at the chart in Figure 2, which is used to discredit the theory that it's the sun and not CO_2 levels, which is the main forcer of the Earth's temperature, you see that the 2002-2014 pause has been mysteriously changed into a period of rapidly-rising temperature (Figure 3).

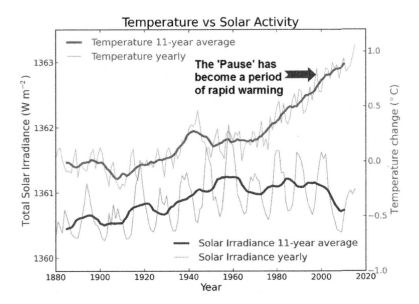

Figure 3 – How the 'pause' became a rise

If we reject the official, ever-rising-temperature chart and accept that the pause did happen as reported at the time, then there is a much better fit between levels of solar irradiance and global temperatures. Though, making this adjustment doesn't explain why temperatures have reportedly risen since the end of the pause in spite of decreasing solar activity. There are several possibilities. Perhaps it really is rising CO_2 which is the main driver of temperature? Perhaps temperatures aren't really rising at all and the supposed 'rise' has been created by official meteorology bodies changing 'raw' (measured') temperatures showing a downwards trend into 'adjusted' temperatures showing a rising trend? (Figure 4).

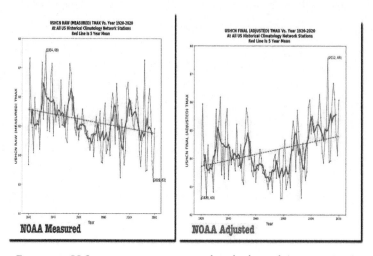

Figure 4 – U.S. temperatures measured and adjusted (1880 to 2019)

Or perhaps temperatures are actually rising because we are in an interglacial, during which we should expect rising temperatures. And perhaps this interglacial is caused by the other aspect of the Earth's relation to the sun – the changes in orbit and tilt due to Milankovitch Cycles?

MILANKOVITCH CYCLES

The term 'Milankovitch Cycles' is named after Serbian astronomer and geophysicist Milutin Milanković who proposed that there were three main variations in the Earth's movement through space which influenced the Earth's climate. These were eccentricity, axial tilt and precession (Figure 5).

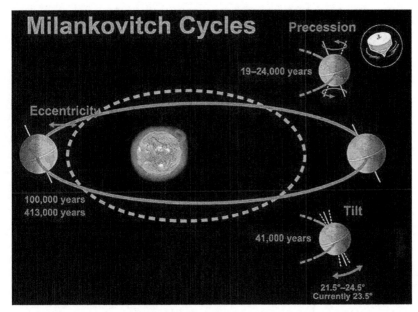

Figure 5 – The three Milankovitch Cycles44 (from Universetoday.com)

Eccentricity describes the earth's orbit around the sun. Axial tilt refers to the angle of the Earth's axis which varies from 21.5 degrees (some sources say 22.1 degrees) to 24.5 degrees over a 41,000-year cycle. Precession is a wobble in the Earth's rotational axis in relation to stars like Polaris and Vega. All three cycles affect the way and amounts of solar irradiation that reach the Earth.

It is believed that axial tilt affects the Earth's seasons. At the minimum tilt of 21.5 degrees, the Earth's seasons should be less severe with warm summers and cool winters. At the maximum tilt of 24.5 degrees, seasons should be more extreme with hotter summers and much colder winters. Precession is believed to alter the relative lengths of summers and winters. But the key Milankovitch Cycle in terms of its influence on the Earth's climate is probably the Earth's orbital eccentricity.

The Earth's orbit around the sun is an ellipse. Over a period of 95,000 to 125,000 years, this ellipse varies between nearly circular and more elliptical. It has been estimated that when the Earth's orbit around the sun is nearly circular, its distance from the sun varies between 91 million miles and 94.5 million miles. When the orbit is at its most elliptical, the distance varies between 80 million miles and 116 million miles (Figure 6).

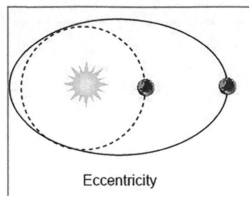

Eccentricity

Figure 6 – Orbital eccentricity45 (from Energy Education)

The key point with orbital eccentricity is that it has been estimated that the heating effect of the sun's radiation can vary due to the changing distance between the Earth and the sun, thus driving changes in the Earth's temperature. Some sources have calculated that the variation in solar irradiation may be as much as between around 270 W/m² and 408 W/m².[46]

Many scientists believe that the 95,000 to 125,000 cycles in solar eccentricity closely match the periods of glaciation and interglacials over at least the last 800,000 years (Figure 7).

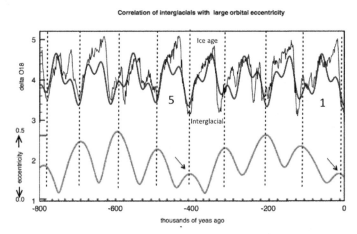

Figure 7 – Interglacials and glaciations[47] (800,000 years)

Clearly the three Milankovitch Cycles are too long-term to have any effect of the Earth's climate since industrialisation. However, one of the key charts used by the climate catastrophists to supposedly 'prove' that atmospheric CO_2 has been the main driver of climate change in the past was the alleged fit between periods of warming and CO_2 increases over the last 800,000 years (Figure 8).

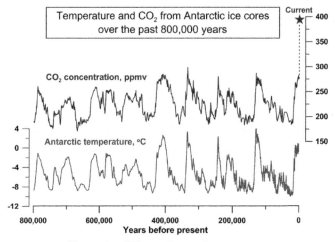

Figure 8 – CO_2 vs Antarctic temperature

But the claim that CO_2 has been the main driver of temperature doesn't make sense. The climate doom-mongers propose what we could call a 'linear relationship' – rising CO_2 leads to warming which leads to more CO_2 being released by the oceans which leads to more warming and thus more CO_2 and so on. But if this were true, why did the warming keep stopping and be replaced by cooling? The Milankovitch Cycle theory of eccentricity in the Earth's orbit around the sun in 95,000- to 125,000-year cycles gives a much more plausible explanation of the cyclical nature of the last 800,000 years of warming and cooling.

Of course, identifying that it was the Earth's orbital eccentricity varying the distance between the Earth and the sun, and not changing CO_2 levels, which was responsible for the last 800,000 years of warming and cooling, doesn't necessarily mean that modern-day warming is not caused by post-industrialisation rising atmospheric CO_2 levels. But it does at least drive a rather large and impressive coach and horses through the climate alarmists' claims that previous climate changes were caused by changes in atmospheric CO_2 levels.

WHAT ABOUT ALL THE OTHER CYCLES?

Here I've just dealt with the possible influence of Milankovitch Cycles on the Earth's climate. But there are many other cyclical events which also influence the Earth's climate and weather patterns. For example, there is the El Niño. *National Geographic* describes El Niño as follows:

El Niño is a climate pattern that describes the unusual warming of surface waters in the eastern tropical Pacific Ocean. El Nino is the "warm phase" of a larger phenomenon called the El Nino-Southern Oscillation (ENSO). La Nina, the "cool phase" of ENSO, is a pattern that describes the unusual cooling of the region's surface waters. El Niño and La Niña are considered the ocean part of ENSO, while the Southern Oscillation is its atmospheric changes.

El Niño has an impact on ocean temperatures, the speed and strength of ocean currents, the health of coastal fisheries, and local weather from Australia to South America and beyond. El Niño events occur irregularly at two- to seven-year intervals. However, El Niño is not a regular cycle, or predictable in the sense that ocean tides are.

Scientists use the Oceanic Nino Index (ONI) to measure deviations from normal sea surface temperatures. El Niño events are indicated by sea surface temperature increases of more than 0.9° Fahrenheit for at least five successive three-month seasons. The intensity of El Niño events varies from weak temperature increases (about 4–5° F) with only moderate local effects on weather and climate to very strong increases (14–18° F) associated with worldwide climatic changes .

There is also the Atlantic Multi-decadal Oscillation (AMO). The AMO is a natural variability occurring in the North Atlantic Ocean with an estimated period of 60-80 years. It is based upon the average anomalies of sea surface temperatures (SST) in the North Atlantic basin and can lead to changes in sea temperatures of up to 0.5°C irrespective of any warming caused by other temperature forcers such as solar irradiance, atmospheric CO_2 levels or Milankovitch Cycles.

And we shouldn't forget cloud cover. Even leading alarmists have been on record as stating that just a 1% change in cloud cover would alter the Earth's temperature by 0.8°C – that's the same change as the 0.8°C temperature increase that the panicking warmists claim to have measured during the last 100 years. With somewhere between 67% and 68% of the Earth being covered in different types of clouds at any one time and with the constant movement of many different types of clouds making accurate cloud-cover measurements impossible, it may be the case that small changes in cloud cover are actually the main driver of changing temperatures.

Moreover, different types of clouds can both warm or cool the Earth at different times of the day. Some clouds can prevent the sun's radiation reaching the Earth's surface due to the albedo effect – reflecting the sun's rays back into space. Others can act as insulators trapping heat near the Earth's surface – the greenhouse effect. And then there's the possible influence of cosmic particles seeding clouds. If this is happening, then variations in levels of cosmic particles entering the Earth's atmosphere and influencing cloud formation may be a significant forcer of temperature changes.

A recent scientific study in April 2020 claimed: 'The shortwave cloud radioactive effect plays a critical role in the earth's radiation balance, and its global mean magnitude is much larger than the warming effect induced by greenhouse gases.'[48] Similarly, another study in September 2020 proposed:

'The clouds represent a key element within the terrestrial climate system. In fact, clouds may be the most important parameter controlling the radiation budget, and, hence, the Earth climate.'[49]

Even the figure-fiddling, data-manipulating, global-warming-preaching NASA admits: 'Other important forcings of Earth's climate system include such "variables" as clouds, airborne particulate matter, and surface brightness. Each of these varying features of Earth's environment has the capacity to exceed the warming influence of greenhouse gases.'

These and other climatic phenomena suggest that the mantra of CO_2-haters that rising atmospheric CO_2 is the main driver of supposed global warming or climate change or climate emergency or climate crisis or climate extinction or whatever it is called this month may be far too simplistic and may even be wrong.

Then when you add in the fact that the main (~90%) greenhouse gas – water vapour – is impossible to measure accurately as it is not uniformly mixed throughout the atmosphere; that aerosols (small particles) from volcanoes, emissions of sulphates from industry and other sources can absorb and reflect solar and cosmic radiation; that changes in aerosol concentrations can alter cloud reflectivity through their effect on cloud properties; and changing weather patterns will lead to unpredictable climate variations, you have a highly complex, thermodynamic system which will probably not be properly understood for many decades to come, if ever.

CUTE MODELS?

As for the often questionable models used by the climate catastrophists to convince us that we're heading towards an oven-temperature disaster, these have failed to explain temperature changes in the past and have consistently over-estimated likely temperature changes since satellites started being used in the 1970s. Figure 9 comes from testimony given to the U.S. House Committee on Science, Space and Technology by Professor John Christy on 2 February 2016 and compares actual temperatures measured by both balloons and satellites with the predictions of 102 climate model runs using 32 different climate models.

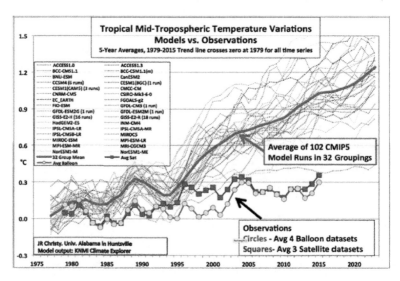

Figure 9 – Average of 102 model runs vs satellite and balloon results (1975-2015)

The upper thick line is the average of the 102 model runs. The two lower thick lines are measurements from balloons (the lowest line with circles on it) and from satellites (the middle line with squares on it).

This comparison showed that the average of the model runs predicted a temperature rise of 0.214°C per decade. But the actual increase was just 0.091°C for satellite measurements and 0.079°C for balloon measurements. So, the models 'over-warm' the Earth's temperature by a factor of between 2.3 (satellites) and 2.7 (balloons) times.

When this comparison between climate models and reality was run again four years later in 2019, the models were still overestimating global temperatures (Figure 10).

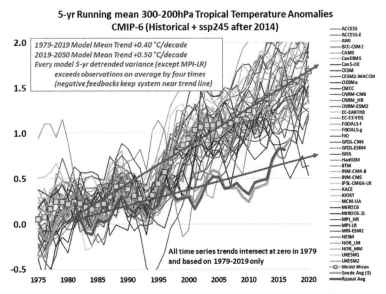

Figure 10 – Comparison of models vs measured temperatures (1979 to 2019)

The top thick line is the average for the models and the models' warming trend. The lower thick lines are the measured temperatures and the measured actual temperature trend.

In spite of evidence from the 2015 comparison showing the models' 2.3 to 2.7 times over-warming, it seems the models weren't adjusted to better reflect reality. This massive overestimation of warming by the climate models is just one of many reasons – including also data manipulation, politicisation of science, baseless exaggeration, desperation of some scientists for media attention and shameless dishonesty – why the doom-mongering claims by the climate catastrophists bear no relation to what is happening in reality.

So, it seems that predictions from failing climate models produced by less than credible supposed 'experts' and exaggerated, distempered media reports from credulous, politically-motivated, headline-hunting journalists are really not the best basis for our politicians making draconian environmental policies which risk wrecking Western economies and impoverishing tens of millions of the people whose interests they were voted into power to protect.

These charts have been lambasted by furious climate alarmists. But there are many like them produced by other climate realists and they all reach a similar conclusion – the climate models based on rising atmospheric CO_2 being the main driver of global temperatures have hugely overestimated the degree of the Earth's warming.

This failure of their models is probably why the climate catastrophists seem to have resorted to blatant 'tampering with the evidence' in desperation to shore up their increasingly creaky, leaky case. They appear to have turned measured raw data cooling trends, which were clearly identified by contemporaneous newspaper reports, into carefully 'adjusted' warming trends (Figure 4 above). And they have eliminated the more than embarrassing (for catastrophists) 2002 to 2014 pause, which even the ultra-warmist IPCC and BBC admitted had happened (until the BBC changed its mind). Almost incredibly, the catastrophists have blatantly turned this well-documented 12-year pause into a period of rapid warming (Figure 3 above).

CHAPTER 12

We've never had it so good

WHY THE DOOM AND GLOOM?

Perhaps one of the strangest aspects of the current doom-and-gloom, we're-headed-for-extinction cult is that it's happening at a time when the human race has never had it so good. If we look at any indicator of mankind's well-being up till the end of 2019 when China, ably assisted by the incompetent, corrupt, sinophiliac and ludicrously misnamed World Health Organisation unleashed the Chinese Wuhan plague on the world, they all point in the same direction – things were getting better for the human race.

In spite of more than thirty years being bombarded by ever more hyperbolic and apocalyptic claims of impending disaster from climate catastrophists wanting to control our lives, mainstream media journalists desperate to advance their own careers and scientifically-challenged politicians eager to increase their own power over us, none of the climate catastrophists' predictions have actually happened.

Polar ice isn't melting. Summer sea ice in the Arctic is declining, but winter sea ice in the Arctic is increasing. Moreover, a small overall decline in Arctic sea ice is being more than compensated for by a much larger 80-billion-tons-a-year increase in massive Antarctic ice cap.

If sea levels are rising at all, which itself is questionable, the rise is probably only somewhere around 7 cms a century. So, if this rise were to continue, which is far from certain, it would take between 1,700 and 2,600 years to reach the 4- to 6-feet rise the catastrophists have warned us would happen by the end of this century – in the next 79 years at the time of writing – flooding coastal cities, leaving many river deltas under water and creating millions of 'climate refugees'.

It's possible the Earth is getting slightly warmer – about 0.6°C (IPCC) to 0.8°C (satellite measurements) a century – as we move through an interglacial. But this tiny increase is unlikely to turn our planet into a burning fiery furnace. Moreover, many more people die from cold each year than die from heat. So a small rise in temperature may actually be a life-saver. Furthermore, there have been drops in temperature as in the Little Cooling of the 1960s and 1970s and there has been the 12-year pause of 2002 to 2014 which both cast doubt on the credibility of the alarmists' simplistic narrative that rising CO_2 inevitably causes rising warming. Even worse, it's not certain we can actually trust the temperature charts being used to terrify us into meek submission to ever more drastic environmental restrictions on our lives as the raw, measured data has clearly been adjusted and manipulated to 'disappear' the high temperatures of the 1920s and 1930s, the low temperatures of the 1960s and 1970s and the pause of 2002 to 2014.

CO2 levels are rising at a rate that hasn't been seen for over 800,000 years. And this is probably due to mankind's CO2 emissions from burning fossil fuels. But there is little evidence that this is the main driver of temperature or climate changes. However, there is clear evidence that this is leading to a greening of the Earth and an increase in agricultural areas as well as an increase in agricultural productivity.

As for wildfires and extreme weather events, there are fewer wildfires burning much less acreage than 30 or 40 years ago and there are fewer floods, fewer hurricanes, fewer tropical cyclones (see Part 2 – The Alarmists' Apocalyptic Warnings). In fact, it's difficult to find a single disastrist prediction that has actually happened.

IT'S GETTING BETTER ALL THE TIME

If we look at the trends detailed on the apolitical website – *Our World in Data* – rather than accepting the overblown and unsubstantiated predictions of climate Armageddon from the climate alarmists, the picture is not one of climate-driven catastrophe. Instead, all we can see are constantly-improving conditions for mankind.

DEATHS FROM NATURAL DISASTERS

We could start with deaths from natural disasters. There has been a dramatic fall since the boiling hot years of the 1920s and 1930s (Figure 1).

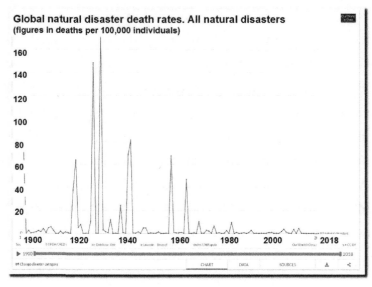

Figure 1 – Deaths from natural disasters (1900 to 2018)

We can also see how many people died by decade in each type of natural disaster (Figure 2).

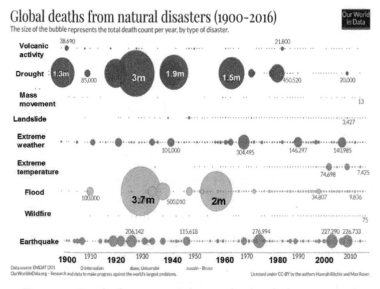

Figure 2 – Deaths from natural disasters by decade (1900 to 2016)

In the hot 1920s and 1930s, over 3 million died in droughts and another 3.7 million in floods. In the cooler 1960s and 1970s, there were about 1.5 million deaths in droughts and around 2 million in floods. Since then, in spite of large increases in human population, there were negligible drought and flood deaths. After the year 2000, the main causes of natural disaster deaths seem to have been earthquakes. So, nothing at all to do with supposed climate change.

CLIMATE CHANGE AND AGRICULTURE

The climate catastrophists seem to get great pleasure from predicting that climate change will devastate agriculture and lead to mass starvation. Here's a typical warning from April 2021:

Yet, if we look at agricultural production from the non-alarmist, more factual *Our World in Data*, we see a quite different picture (Figure 3).

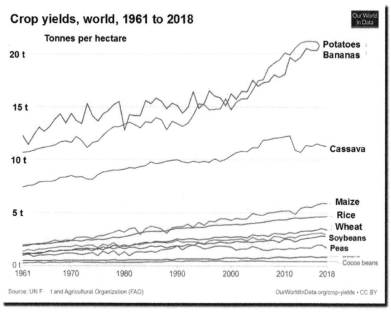

Figure 3 – Crop yields in tonnes per hectare (1961 to 2018)

The climate Armageddonists claim that agricultural productivity has fallen by 21% since 1961. But the real figures of yields per hectare for every major crop have all increased.

Linked to improved agricultural productivity, which the alarmists vehemently deny is happening, is a dramatic fall in undernourishment in every part of the world. Since 2000, the world population has grown from about 6.2 billion to over 7.5 billion. Yet so much extra food has been produced and distributed, that the number of people being adequately fed has shot up from 5.3 billion to 6.7 billion while undernourishment has declined. Between 2000 and 2017, the percent of the world's population that is undernourished has fallen from 13.4% to 8.8%. For Africa the fall is from 23.8% to 18.6% (Figure 4).

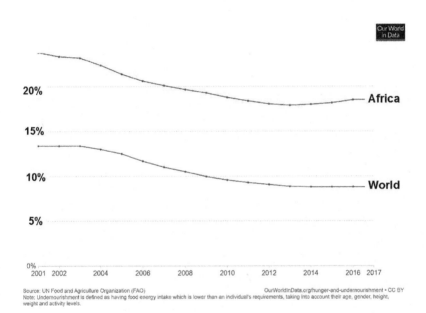

Figure 4 – Undernourishment has declined since 2000

In addition, the number of children dying under the age of five has plunged from 12.6 million a year in 1990, when the world's population was 5.33 billion, to just 5.4 million a year in 2017, when the world's population reached 7.55 billion (Figure 5).

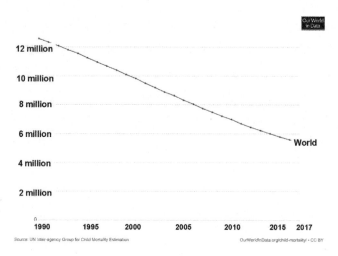

Figure 5 – Deaths of children under five years old

LIVING LONGER, BETTER LIVES

With fewer deaths from natural disasters, more and better food and, of course, huge medical advances, the world's increasing population is benefiting from rising life expectancy (Figure 6).

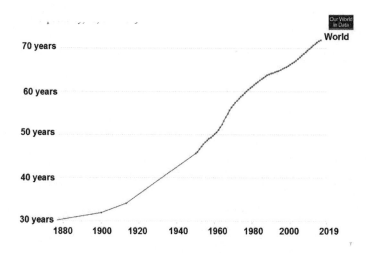

Figure 6 – Life expectancy (1870 to 2019)

Moreover, poverty is being reduced (Figure 7).

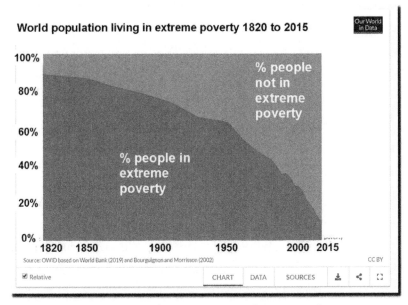

Figure 7 – Reduction in poverty (1820 to 2015)

The lower, darker area on the chart is the percentage of the world's population living in extreme poverty – defined as living on less than $1.90 a day.

WE'VE NEVER HAD IT SO GOOD

I could go on with chart after chart showing improvements in seemingly every aspect of human welfare. But the one thing that is difficult to find on the apolitical *Our World in Data* website is any evidence that global warming or climate change or the climate crisis are having any discernible negative effect on any aspect of human life anywhere in the world.

The climate Cassandras keep telling us that we're headed for total self-destruction. But the opposite seems to be happening. Things are only getting better. It turned out that the original historical/fictional Cassandra was correct in predicting the future destruction of Troy. Her tragedy was that nobody believed her. The climate Cassandras of today, with their hopelessly inaccurate and politicised models and their unhinged forecasts of disasters yet to come, aren't even correct in predicting what has already happened. Yet our tragedy is that, in spite of every prediction the climate catastrophists make being wrong, millions, or even tens of millions, still unswervingly believe every word they say.

Our children are being indoctrinated with the message that they'll all die young from the supposed climate crisis. This is almost a form of child abuse. The truth is that our children will all probably live longer, better, healthier lives than their parents.

We truly seem to be caught in a madhouse in which the opposite of the truth has become the only permitted truth for the woke generation. Meanwhile, the truth has become anathema to those who have been brainwashed into trusting their feelings rather than logical, objective, provable facts and persuaded to always see themselves as victims rather than relishing the joyful reality that their life chances are actually better than any previous generation in human history.

CHAPTER 13

The West's economic suicide

It is difficult to see any real signs of the supposedly 'catastrophic' human-caused climate change in any indicator of human development and quality of life (see Chapter 12 – We've never had it so good). But you can definitely see the effects of the last 30 to 40 years of climate alarmism in what we've done and, more importantly, what we're about to do to our economies and our lifestyles.

For example, due to Western countries closing down cheap and reliable nuclear, coal and gas-fired power plants and replacing them with expensive and unreliable wind and solar power, energy prices in the West are much higher than in our industrial competitors like China and India. For households, Germany has the highest energy prices of any major industrialised country. At $0.36 per kilowatt/hour (kw/h) German consumers pay more than twice as much as domestic consumers in the U.S. and over four times as much as consumers in China, India and Russia (Figure 1).

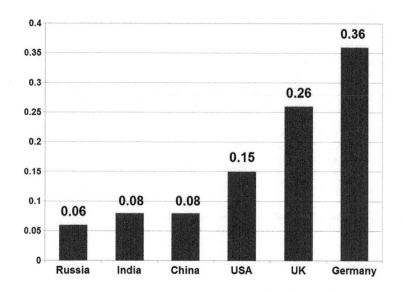

Figure 1 – Household energy prices (2019 $/kw/h)

For industrial electricity users the situation is a bit more complicated as there are often a large range of tariffs and discounts depending on the industry and levels of usage. But it does seem that 94% of German companies are probably paying at least three times more for their power than their competitors in China and India.

U.S. energy prices might also seem inexplicably high. During the Donald Trump presidency, the U.S. became self-sufficient in energy whereas its major competitor, China, imports vast amounts of oil, gas and coal. Yet U.S. energy prices are around twice the level of those in China. Part of the explanation for this price difference could be seen by what is happening in possibly the U.S.'s most progressive, intersectionally-aware, woke state and formerly the world's fifth largest economy – California. An article in *Forbes* magazine explains:[50]

'California now imports most of its crude oil from overseas (since the extraction of its ample local oil resources are practically banned) and it imports nearly a third of its electricity from neighbouring states (since nuclear and natural gas-fuelled power plants are progressively shutdown by legislation). Between 2011 and 2017, California's electricity prices rose five times faster than they did nationally and now Californians pay 60 percent more, on average, than the rest of the nation, for residential, commercial and industrial electricity.'

California's Governor has admitted that the state's move away from fossil fuels has contributed to California's rolling electricity blackouts. Nevertheless on 23 September 2020, California's Governor signed an executive order banning the sale of new petrol-powered vehicles within 15 years to reduce air pollution and reach the state's goals for cutting greenhouse gases. A spokesperson for the U.S. Environmental Protection Agency commented: 'California's record of rolling blackouts – unprecedented in size and scope – coupled with recent requests to neighbouring states for power begs the question of how you expect to run an electric car fleet, that will come with significant increases in electricity demand, when you can't even keep the lights on today.'[51]

Partly due to increasing energy prices along with other high-tax, anti-business, ultra-woke policies, between June 2019 and June 2020, around 135,000 people left the once 'Golden State'. Moreover, Oracle, Palantir and Hewlett-Packard Enterprise were among the estimated 13,000 companies that have moved out of

California since 2014 and relocated to more business-friendly states like Texas.

Australia also provides a possibly interesting case study in the effects of moving away from cheap and reliable fossil fuels and imposing ever more burdensome taxes on consumers. In 2019, about 58% of Australia's electricity came from coal-fired power stations. This was down from 80% in 1993. Australia is the world's largest coal exporter and, until a series of spats with an increasingly expansionist and aggressive China in 2020, was by far China's largest coal supplier. In 2019, China was also generating about 58% of its electricity from coal – about 40% of which came from Australia. Yet in spite of both countries having almost identical percentages of their electricity coming from coal in 2019, electricity prices in Australia at $0.25 per kw/h were three times those in China.

It's often quite difficult to know how electricity prices are structured. But we do know that the main reason for the high and ever-rising prices in developed countries is the large number of extra charges that are added onto users' bills to pay for our rulers' apparent loathing of the idea that we ordinary people can benefit from cheap and reliable fossil-fuel energy. In Germany, for example, there are no fewer than eight different costs consumers have to pay (Figure 2).

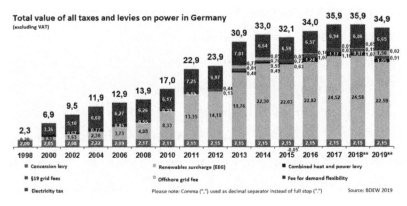

Figure 2 – The taxes and levies added to German power bills (not including VAT)

German electricity users have to pay a Concession Levy, Grid Fees, an Electricity Tax, a Renewables Energy Surcharge, an Offshore Grid Fee, a Combined Heat and Power levy and a Fee for Current Flexibility. And then, of course, you have to add VAT on top of all the other charges. All these various and imaginative charges have increased almost every year. Due to all these extra charges, power prices in Germany have shot up 68% in the last 15 years and more than 17% of German households are estimated to be in 'energy poverty' – not having sufficient income to heat their homes properly.

Another reason for Germany's high energy prices is that the country can boast one of the strangest political decisions affecting energy supply in any country in recent years. Within days of the March 2011 Japan Fukushima Daiichi nuclear disaster, when the nuclear power station was wrecked by a tsunami, there were large anti-nuclear protests in several major German cities. In response, on 29 May 2011, German Chancellor Angela Merkel decided to accelerate the closure of all Germany's nuclear power stations, shutting them all by 2022 instead of the original date of 2036. Eight of Germany's seventeen operating reactors were closed that year. Merkel claimed that this was yet another of her brilliant policy decisions: 'As the first big industrialized nation, we can achieve such a transformation toward efficient and renewable energies, with all the opportunities that brings for exports, developing new technologies and jobs.'

What Mrs Merkel may have 'forgotten' to mention to German electricity users was how much this grandstanding, holier-than-thou early closure would cost them. The German Ministry for Economics put the cost of replacing the lost nuclear power at more than €55 billion over ten years. But other organizations in Germany predicted Germans would have to fork out around €250 billion over the next decade – €6,250 per household. In addition, you have to consider that in 2016 the German Federal Constitutional Court (*Bundesverfassungsgericht*) ruled that nuclear plant operators affected by the accelerated phase-out of nuclear power were eligible for what was termed 'adequate' compensation. So the plant operators could sue the German Government under civil law. At least six cases have been registered with courts in Germany. This means that German electricity users can look forward to paying many tens of billions more for their power thanks to the environmentalists' and Merkel's post-Fukushima anti-nuclear war.

If only someone could have loaned the anti-nuclear protestors and Chancellor Merkel an atlas, then they and she might have seen that Japan consisted of several islands with a coastline of 29,751 kilometres, while Germany is largely landlocked and only has 2,389 kilometres of coastline. This would make Germany rather less vulnerable to tsunamis than Japan. Moreover, most of Germany's nuclear power stations, unlike those in Japan, were hundreds of miles from the sea.

In addition, someone could have explained to the anti-nuclear environmental protestors and Chancellor Merkel that the word tsunami is composed of the Japanese words "tsu" (which means harbour) and "nami" (which means "wave"). Germans are usually rather good at inventing new long melodic compound words like *Arbeiterunfallverischerungsgesetz* and *Nahrungsmittelunverträglichkeit*. But, as far as I know, there isn't even a word in German for tsunami as they've never had one in the whole of human history. That would have been another hint for the anti-nuclearists and Chancellor Merkel that there really wasn't too much in common between what happened to part of Japan's nuclear power industry following a tsunami and what might happen in Germany which had never experienced a tsunami.

Furthermore, perhaps one of Merkel's minions could even have helpfully pointed out to the over-excited environmental anti-nuclear activists and their Chancellor that Japan is situated on the Pacific 'Ring of Fire' and is thus subject to frequent seismic events like earthquakes and tsunamis? Germany, on the other hand, is in the much more seismically-stable Europe and probably hasn't experienced a major earthquake or tsunami in the last few hundred million years, if ever.

YOU AIN'T SEEN NOTHING YET

Up till now, our rulers' tinkering with closing inexpensive, reliable fossil-fuel electricity sources, replacing them with hopelessly unpredictable, inefficient and unreliable supposed 'renewables' and dreaming up ever more exotic taxes on our energy use is a tiny, almost inconsequential *amuse bouche* compared to the main course which is about to be dumped on us as our rulers scramble to fulfil the bombastic, virtue-signalling, absurdly unrealisable promises they so enthusiastically made on our behalf at the 2015 UN-driven Paris Agreement on Climate Change.

The Paris climate conference on 30 November to 12 December 2015 was a fairly modest affair by normal climate conference standards with only about 20,000 accredited participants. In comparison, no fewer than 30,000 good folk flew, all expenses paid, to Rio de Janeiro in June 1992 to save the planet. Although the Paris conference does seem to have been a lot more popular with climate activists, politicians, bureaucrats and journalists than the 2009 Copenhagen Climate Conference which only attracted about 15,000 delegates. But perhaps that's understandable? After all, the weather, food and entertainment possibilities in dull northern Copenhagen are rather dismal in December (average temperature 1°C) compared to the climate and opportunities for some serious culinary pleasures and adult fun in much more exotic Rio de Janeiro in June (average temperature 26°C).

At the 2015 Paris Conference, representatives of more than 190 countries signed up to taking actions to supposedly keep the rise in global average temperature to below 2°C (3.6°F) above pre-industrial levels and to pursue efforts to limit the increase to 1.5°C (2.7°F) to 'substantially reduce the risks and impacts of climate change.'

The Paris Agreement committed each country to provide what were called Nationally Determined Contributions (NDCs) explaining what actions their country would take to keep global temperatures to the goal of under 2°C compared to pre-industrial levels.

The usual suspects in the climate-alarmist media naturally declared the Paris Agreement a huge success which would save mankind from otherwise certain extinction. But the NDCs were not legally binding and, in the years since 2015, have been sniggeringly ignored by most of the countries who signed up.

In contrast to the obviously impressed journalists lauding our leaders for saving the world at the Paris climate jamboree, a climate realist might be tempted to view the whole 20,000-attendee, CO_2-belching affair with a certain degree of caution. To simplify slightly, one could split the country leaders signing up into three main groups.

There were the industrialised countries of the West – the EU27, the UK, Australia and New Zealand – which seem to have taken the whole thing seriously. Some of these countries have even enshrined their NDCs into law. Thus they have forced their countries to achieve their NDC promises. As for the U.S., it sensibly withdrew from the Paris Agreement under President Trump. But the U.S. has now rejoined under President Harris, sorry, I meant President Biden, of course.

Another group of Paris signatories consisted of the larger industrialising countries – China, India, Indonesia, Thailand,

Vietnam – which probably looked on with a mixture of amusement, amazement and delight as the rich West, through some perverted sense of guilt for its own success, gaily committed economic suicide. These countries had no intention of ever reducing their greenhouse gas emissions. On the contrary, countries like China, Indonesia, Vietnam, South Korea, the Philippines and Pakistan were busy building a lot more coal-fired power stations to provide their citizens and companies with cheap, reliable electricity. And most were probably looking forward to even more industries and jobs moving away from the energy-expensive industrialised countries to their part of the world.

Then there were the often impoverished Third-World countries, many of whose leaders were already billionaires thanks largely to generous foreign aid handouts from the rich West. These countries were pantingly eager to get their hands on as much as possible of a proposed $100 billion-a-year fund, intended to run from 2020 to 2025, to supposedly help these countries adapt to and mitigate the disasters – rising sea levels, hotter temperatures, more storms and droughts etc etc – that the climate catastrophists predicted anthropogenic climate change would inevitably inflict on them. At UN-sponsored climate talks in Madrid in December 2020, the Maldives and other vulnerable countries pushed for concrete progress on fresh funding to help them deal with disasters and longer-term damage linked to climate change. That's the same Maldives that has just built a third runway at its main airport to accommodate larger aircraft and which, in 2022, should be opening a new passenger terminal to increase capacity from one million to 7.3 million passengers a year.

THE FINANCIAL AND HUMAN COSTS OF 'NET ZERO'

The leaders of the few countries which are actually trying to implement their Paris Agreement NDCs often talk about achieving carbon neutrality or carbon 'net zero' by some point in the near future – often 2050. Though it's doubtful that many of the virtue-signalling, posturing politicians and compliant bureaucrats intent on implementing 'net zero' even understand what the term means, how much it will cost and the implications of imposing it on their not always enthusiastic or convinced populations. The term 'net zero' means achieving a balance between the carbon emitted into the atmosphere and the carbon removed from it. This balance – or net zero – will happen when the amount of carbon we add to the atmosphere is no more than the amount removed. Given that most advanced industrialised economies are reliant on fossil fuels – coal, oil and gas – for most of their energy and transport, the costs and required lifestyle changes to achieve the supposed glorious net zero goal could appear to be more than horrendous for their citizens.

For the U.S., the cost was reported by the climate-catastrophist *CNN* at somewhere between $1 trillion and $2 trillion a year up to 2050.[52] If we take the lower estimate of $1 trillion a year and if I've got the right number of zeros, then that's a cost of over $8,000 per year for almost thirty years for each of the U.S.'s 123,000,000 households.

For the last five or more years, the UK government seems to have done everything possible to block *Freedom of Information* requests trying to find out the true cost of the UK achieving net zero. The only figure the government will release is an out-of-date estimate of about £50 billion a year – a paltry £1,786 per year for for thirty years for each of the UK's 28 million households. But this £50 billion a year is widely suspected to be a deceptively and deliberately large underestimate. For example the National Grid, the company that manages the network and distribution of electricity and gas that powers all the country's homes and businesses, has calculated that just to upgrade its network would cost about £3 trillion – that's almost £100 billion a year up to 2050.

In addition, we have to factor in the costs of scrapping petrol and diesel cars and replacing them with electric cars. Even if prices of electric cars fall as more are produced, that could easily cost £10,000 to £20,000 per car above the cost of a petrol car. Many homes will need to install a fast electric vehicle charger – another £2,400 each. There's also the cost of replacing efficient and responsive gas-fired cooking and central heating in 23 million of the UK's 28 million homes with less efficient, less powerful and less responsive heat pumps which reportedly can take hours to warm up and only warm homes to 17°C to 19°C. That's between £10,000 and £18,000 per household for an air-source heat pump and over £35,000 per house for a ground-source heat pump. You may also need to rip up your floors to install underfloor heating with your heat pump just to get your home to a decent liveable temperature. That's a few thousand pounds more and an awful lot of dirt, noise and disruption you probably would rather avoid. If you don't want to install underfloor heating, you'll probably have to replace all your standard radiators with new larger ones as heat pumps won't give sufficient heat with your existing radiators – another few thousand pounds down the eco-drain.

Moreover, there would be new energy efficiency regulations for homes. In the UK, regulations mean that, since 1 April 2018, private landlords may not rent out domestic properties on new tenancies to new or existing tenants if the Energy Performance Certificate (EPC) rating is F or G. It may soon even become illegal to sell any home which doesn't reach the required energy efficiency standards. An organisation called the Energy Technologies Institute has estimated that just retrofitting insulation to the UK housing stock alone would cost over £2 trillion.[53]

Moreover, there will be new taxes. The government will need to replace the revenue it will lose from fuel duty falling as more people are forced to buy electric cars. For example, in 2020 one Australian state decided to impose a 2.5 cents per kilometre tax for fully electric vehicles and 2 cents per kilometre for hybrid vehicles. It's not difficult to imagine that other states and other countries will be watching this with interest and designing similar taxes to discourage us from using our cars too much. Plus there will be new taxes to save the planet by discouraging us from supposedly environmentally-damaging activities like flying or eating meat.

Furthermore, it's not obvious that the UK government has thought of telling us that its net zero by 2050 plans include things like a reduction in cars in the UK from around 33 million to just 20 million and a reduction in meat consumption of 20% by 2030 and a further 15% by 2050. Still, as the EU approved the use of protein-rich beetle larvae as a snack or ingredient as an environmentally-conscious new food at the start of May 2021 and a regulation authorising dried yellow mealworms as a food was planned to be adopted a few weeks later, we can all look forward to replacing planet-destroying steaks and burgers with delicious, planet-saving, nutritious insects.

There are probably three new words we're all going to become reluctantly familiar with – eco-nudging, eco-coercion and eco-dictatorship. An example of eco-nudging might be increasing electricity prices for anyone without a 'smart meter' to encourage them to install one or simply increasing taxes on domestic gas to push households to replace quiet, efficient, warm gas central heating with noisy, less efficient, not so warm heat pumps. Eco-coercion might be banning the sale of gas central-heating boilers or petrol cars or petrol lawn-mowers. Eco-dictatorship could look like government-employed 'energy monitors' examining individual households' energy use and using smart meters to either increase prices for supposedly 'wasteful' households or even cutting electricity supply to any households deemed by the 'energy monitors' to be using too much energy as those households might be guilty of a new crime called perhaps 'deliberately harming the environment'.

The UK's *Guardian* newspaper tells us we should all be excited about this utopian insect-munching future where:

'the populace would whizz past in their electric cars, to and from homes equipped with induction stoves and heat pumps. The air would be near pristine. Hundreds of thousands of people who would have prematurely died from the toxic fossil-fuel age would still be alive.'[54]

The newspaper shamelessly also claims: 'Overall the cost is surprisingly low.'[55] However, people who don't read the *Guardian* may get the impression that their governments will be using higher prices, more taxes and new laws to enforce a kind of energy rationing, a bit like the food rationing in the UK during and after World War II.

The *Guardian*'s picture of the coming extremely cheap, carbon-neutral paradise is echoed by the UK's public broadcaster, the *Guardian*-reading BBC, which enthuses about the joys of our zero-carbon future: 'A quarter of Britain covered in trees, quieter roads, healthier lifestyles and holidays by high-speed rail. That's how the United Kingdom could look as a result of its bid to be carbon neutral by 2050.' Though thankfully, the BBC does accept that, if you want to go to Australia for your holidays, you would still have to take a plane rather than a high-speed train.[56]

HOW TO DESTROY JOBS?

It should be obvious to anyone except for our politicians and climate activists that, if we are to have an economy which can create jobs, we need to make things at competitive prices that we can sell to other countries. Here I'll just take the UK as an example of where energy costs might be heading as we're dragged kicking and screaming towards net-zero nirvana. A similar calculation can be done for any other Western country whose leaders are hell-bent on reaching the fabled net zero.

As we've seen, at $0.26 per kw/h energy users (industry and

households) in the UK are already paying around three times as much for their energy as countries like China ($0.08 per kw/h), India ($0.08 per kw/h) and Indonesia ($0.10 per kw/h) which now make most of the stuff UK consumers buy. Were the UK's energy costs to rise any further, this would clearly do even more damage to what little is left of the country's manufacturing sector in particular and the economy in general. If we put aside for a moment the eye-watering direct costs each household will have to pay for things like heat pumps, improved insulation, replacing most of their electric wiring, electric cars, electric vehicle charging points and so on and just look at what is likely to happen to our energy bills to pay for our scientifically-challenged, politicians', our anti-West climate activists' and our brainwashed school-children's Shangri-la of achieving net zero by 2050, what appears is far from pleasant.

Currently, UK industry pays around £13 billion a year for energy, the service sector about £17 billion and households £36 billion. That's a total of £66 billion a year. As mentioned above, the National Grid, the company that manages the network and distribution of electricity and gas that powers all the country's homes and businesses, has calculated that just to upgrade its network would cost about £3 trillion – that's almost £100 billion a year up to 2050. This £100 billion will have to be paid for by increasing the country's energy bills. It doesn't require a mathematical genius to work out that adding up to £100 billion a year to the £66 billion UK energy consumers already pay for their energy is going to more than double energy bills for companies and households.

The move into renewable is already pushing up industry's energy costs in most Western countries. For example, in the UK industry's energy costs have almost tripled since 2004 (Figure 3).[57]

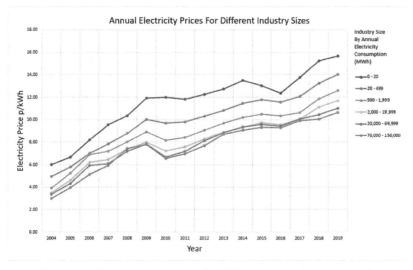

Figure 3 – Rising energy prices for UK companies (2004 to 2019)

Perversely, this massive rise in industry's energy costs has happened at a time when the world has been awash with fossil fuels mainly due to the U.S. achieving energy self-sufficiency thanks to fracking and therefore not needing to buy either oil or gas from the Middle East. The move towards net zero by 2050 is going to hugely accelerate the increase in industry's energy costs. As far as I am aware, none of our politicians or climate catastrophists or schoolchildren have bothered to explain to us how Western companies are going to survive in a competitive world when Western energy prices shoot up from around three to four times the level the West's competitors pay to six, eight or even ten times those of competitor countries.

Our rulers in the West promise us that their brilliant environmental policies will create millions of new and exciting 'green jobs'. But studies done in Spain suggested that each 'green job' cost Spanish taxpayers around $774,000 in subsidies and that for every job created in the 'green economy' around 2.2 jobs were lost in the traditional economy due to increasing energy prices making Spanish companies uncompetitive.[58] Moreover, due to rising energy costs in the West, many of the new 'green jobs' will actually be created in countries with low energy costs who will supply many of the solar panels, wind turbines, electric cabling and heat pumps that our governments will force us to install. For example, in 2021 around 70% of all the world's solar cells for solar panels were being made in China and Taiwan. Several Western countries, including the UK, already proudly boast that they are lowering their CO_2 emissions. But what most have really done is to export jobs and thus their CO_2 emissions to countries with cheaper energy. As the West's energy costs continue to rise to pay for the lemming-like rush to net zero, this process of deliberate economic immiseration is destined to continue and even accelerate.

AN EXERCISE IN FUTILITY?

While the West nobly and pointlessly tries to cut its CO_2 emissions to supposedly save the planet, the rest of the world keeps on increasing the amount of CO_2 it is pouring into the atmosphere (Figure 4).

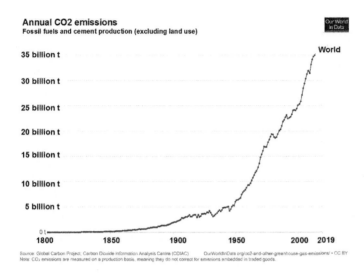

Figure 4 – World CO2 emissions

Looking in more detail, we can see that CO2 emissions are falling in the U.S. and Europe and shooting up in China, India and Asia (Figure 5).

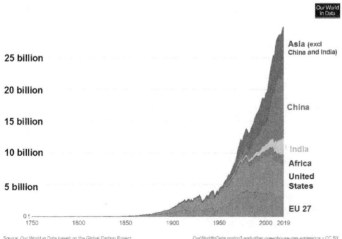

Figure 5 – CO2 emissions from the major economies

CO2 emissions from Africa are very limited at the moment. But it is estimated that at least 70% of Africa's 1.2 billion population currently don't have access to a regular electricity supply – that's 840 million people. According to United Nations population projections, by 2050, when the West hopes to reach net zero CO2, there will be over 2 billion Africans who will all want electricity. A few wind turbines and solar panels here and there aren't going to satisfy this almost unimaginable increase in demand for electricity. Anyone who imagines even a fraction of that demand can be supplied without a massive increase in CO2 emissions from fossil fuels in Africa really hasn't, to put it mildly, thought things through.

As for China, anyone who believes the Chinese have any intention of limiting their CO2 emissions hasn't been paying attention to what is actually happening in the world. Our rulers keep assuring us that China is really trying to decrease its CO2 emissions:

The White House
Office of the Press Secretary

For Immediate Release   November 11, 2014

U.S.-China Joint Announcement on Climate Change

Beijing, China, 12 November 2014

3.   Today, the Presidents of the United States and China announced their respective post-2020 actions on climate change, recognizing that these actions are part of the longer range effort to transition to low-carbon economies, mindful of the global temperature goal of 2°C. The United States intends to achieve an economy-wide target of reducing its emissions by 26%-28% below its 2005 level in 2025 and to make best efforts to reduce its emissions by 28%. China intends to achieve the peaking of CO2 emissions around 2030 and to make best efforts to peak early and intends to increase the share of non-fossil fuels in primary energy consumption to around 20% by 2030. Both sides intend to continue to work to increase ambition over time.

But as with almost everything we're told about climate change, the truth is precisely the opposite of what our rulers and their propagandist, climate-change-alarmist media claim:

China's CO2 emissions are now almost double those of the U.S. and are increasing rapidly (Figure 6).

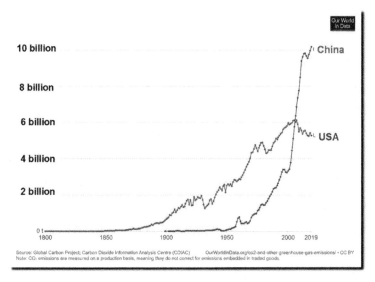

Figure 6 – CO2 emissions China vs USA (Tons CO2 per year)

So, while Western leaders dream up ever more complex, expensive and job-destroying schemes, such as the USA's 'Green New Deal', to 'decarbonise' their economies and impoverish their people, increasing CO_2 emissions from the rest of the world are destined to dwarf any reductions made by the West. If ever there has been an exercise in total futility, the West's attempt to reach net zero by 2050 must surely be it.

THE WEST'S 'MOUNT VESUVIUS MOMENT'?

In the 10 October 2020 edition of the U.S. Forbes magazine, there was a rather jolly article titled: 'The West Intends Energy Suicide: Will It Succeed?' This title pretty much sums up the act of extraordinary self-harm that we in the West are inflicting on ourselves in order to combat something – CO_2-driven global warming or climate change or climate crisis or whatever – that isn't even happening.

Perhaps not since the Romans thought it would be a great idea to build a city around the base of Mount Vesuvius has any group of people made such an idiotic decision. The only difference between the Romans and us is that, apart from the occasional rumbling deep in the mountain, the Romans had no idea that Mount Vesuvius would soon spectacularly blow its top. We in the advanced West, on the other hand, can clearly see how we are enthusiastically rushing to our own self-inflicted economic and societal self-destruction. But we bravely/suicidally (delete as appropriate) carry on regardless.

CHAPTER 14

The renewables mirage

TRASHING THE ENVIRONMENT?

In the previous chapter, I tried to detail some of the appalling economic costs and consequences of our political panjandrums' abject and unnecessary genuflecting to the politicised, figure-fiddling, alarmist supposed climatologists and the woke, howling, eye-bulging masses of climate catastrophists and extinctionists. In this chapter, I'd like to touch on how the policies being pushed by the deluded, environmentally-ignorant climate warriors will be massively destructive for our environment.

The three main current supposedly low-CO_2 or zero-CO_2, environmentally-friendly replacements for fossil fuels are probably biofuels, wind turbines and solar farms. There is also hydro-electricity. But most of the best sites in the West are already being used. So, few projections of future energy sources for Western countries foresee any significant increase in hydro power.

WATER DISASTER! MADE IN CHINA

It's a different story for hydro-electricity in China. The Mekong springs up from the Tibetan Plateau in China and flows to the South China Sea through Myanmar, Thailand, Laos, Cambodia, and Vietnam. Around 60 million people depend on the river for fishing, farming and transportation.

But there's a problem. China and Laos are furiously building dams on the Mekong and its tributaries – partly to harness hydro-electric power and partly to provide water for agricultural irrigation. China has built seven hydropower dams on the upper Mekong River (known as the Lancang in China), and plans to build at least 21 more. Laos, one of the region's poorest countries, plans to turn itself into "the battery of Southeast Asia" by building dozens of hydroelectric dams on the Mekong River and its tributaries and selling the power to neighbouring countries. In 2020, Laos reportedly had 46 such power plants operating and 54 more planned or under construction.

Dams disrupt the migration of fish, preventing them from reaching their spawning grounds upstream and hampering their natural life cycles. This, in turn, could significantly affect fish production in the Mekong, home to the world's largest inland fishery. Experts have predicted up to a 40% reduction in Mekong fish stocks by 2020, and up to 80% by 2040 as a result of hydropower dams in the region. And water extracted for irrigating agricultural land, of course, reduces the water flowing downstream of the dams.

Moreover sediment is critical to the health of the river and essential for replenishing fish life. For Vietnam, the Mekong is crucial – a source from which the country draws approximately 50% of its foodstuffs – and which contributes more than 23% of its GDP. Vietnamese ecologist Nguyen Huu Thien was quoted as saying: 'I am not sure how Vietnam can survive as a nation without the delta.'

What the Chinese and the Laotians are doing to the Mekong with their damn dam-building to get more supposedly CO_2-free environmentally-friendly electricity, so loved by environmental activists in the West, is actually going to be an act of massive environmental and economic vandalism on a level with what the Soviets did to the once huge (68,000 km²) and now almost non-existent Aral Sea:

NO TO NUCLEAR

Then there's the most sensible, cleanest, most reliable, CO_2-free power source of all – nuclear power. But as many of the climate alarmist activists come from environmental organisations, which originated from anti-nuclear protest groups, they're generally rather allergic to any talk of building new nuclear facilities. This is a bit of a pity really as the technology, which is used in nuclear submarines, could probably be quickly adapted to building a series of inexpensive mini land-based nuclear plants which could supply constant, reliable and CO_2-free electricity without wrecking the environment. That just leaves us with biofuels, wind and solar which, we are assured by those who know what's good for us, will save humanity from extinction by replacing planet-wrecking fossil fuels with allegedly clean, low-CO_2 or CO_2-free renewable energy.

ECONOMIC IDIOCY?

It may be worth starting by suggesting that, if biofuels or wind turbines or solar panels had ever made any economic sense, hundreds or even thousands of private companies would have already sprung up to make, sell and install them. As this didn't happen, governments and organisations like the EU have had to use extra taxes, legal action and massive enforced taxpayer subsidies to drive us to use fuels that never had any economic rationale and thus were purely pushed on us to achieve environmental goals.

BIOFUELS — A CRIME AGAINST HUMANITY?

Biofuels were probably the first alternative to fossil fuels which our political elites forced on us by using legal coercion. So, biofuels perhaps provide a good case study in how flawed science promoted by misguided, politicised, often anti-capitalist environmental activists led politicians to enact policies that were both illogical and destructive. Yet, as the evidence mounted proving the policies were wrong, those responsible for them could not reverse them as to do so would mean admitting they had made a mistake – and that's something politicians, cravenly obedient careerist bureaucrats and holier-than-thou activists can never do.

In 2005, the U.S. Congress enacted the Renewable Fuel Standard which required fuel refiners to mix 7.5 billion gallons of ethanol into gasoline by 2012. At the time, Americans used around 133 billion gallons of gasoline. So the part of ethanol represented about 5.6% of each gallon sold. Prior to that, the EU had already passed regulations requiring first that 2.7% of transport fuel consisted of biofuels. This was then raised to 5%. Then in March 2007, the EU went further and mandated that 10% of all fuel used in transport in the EU must consist of biofuels by 2020 and that this must reach 14% by 2030.

The logic for adding biofuels to petrol (gasoline) and diesel was satisfyingly simple. Firstly, ethanol in petrol emitted about 33% fewer greenhouse gases than ordinary petrol and B20 (20% biodiesel) emitted about 15% fewer greenhouse gases than pure fossil-fuel diesel. Moreover when growing, plants extract CO_2 from the atmosphere and then when burned in vehicles, that CO_2 is returned to the atmosphere. This allowed the climate catastrophists to create a pleasing narrative proving that biofuels were CO_2-neutral and thus obviously stupendously good for the planet. However, this scenario didn't take account of all the CO_2 emitted by things like producing the crops for biofuels, fertilising them, harvesting them and the energy required to turn the crops into biofuels. One group of experts calculated that the production of biofuels emitted at least three times more CO_2 than the use of biofuels saved.[59]

Then there was a further more than embarrassing problem. Depending on the percentage of biofuel used, biofuels resulted in a 15% to 27% reduction in fuel economy. So, while biofuels emitted fewer greenhouse gases per litre/gallon used, when judged on how much CO_2 they released per kilometre/mile driven, they gave off as much, if not more, greenhouse gases than pure fossil fuel.

But the biggest problem with biofuels is that they resulted in between 2.5% and 4% (depending on which source you use) of the world's arable land being transferred from food production to producing feedstock for biofuels for cars and lorries. In the 21st Century about 9 million people a year are believed to die from malnutrition and hunger-related diseases. These 9 million deaths include around 3.1 million children – one dying from hunger every ten seconds. We can clearly see how the increasing use of biofuels helped push up food prices from around the year 2000 (Figure 1).[60]

Figure 1 – UN Food and Agriculture Organization Food Price Index (1990 to 2015)

In October 2007 as food prices rose, the United Nation's Special Rapporteur on Food criticised the EU's policy saying it was: 'a crime against humanity to divert arable land to the production of crops which are then burned for fuel.' In 2008, as food prices soared, the World Bank's chief economist claimed that switching food-growing land to biofuels was responsible for most of the more than 140% rise in food prices between 2002 and 2008. Even the climate catastrophist IPCC has admitted that biofuels were hurting the world's poor: 'Increasing demand for biofuels shifts land from food to fuel production, which may increase food prices disproportionally affecting the poor.'[61] It has been estimated that the land set aside for crops for biofuels could have produced enough food for somewhere between 690 and 750 million people. That's partly an over-simplistic criticism. There is probably enough food in the world to feed everyone. Much of the world's hunger is a result of Third-World corruption, kleptocracy, governmental incompetence and tribal and religious war – not a lack of food availability.

However, looking forward into the future, if the population in many undeveloped countries keeps doubling every 22 or so years, the West increasingly replacing food crops with biofuel crops will start to cause food supply problems. Many readers will remember the Band Aid record 'Do they know it's Christmas?' and the associated Live Aid concert from 1984/5 to raise money for starving Ethiopians. At the time, the population of Ethiopia was around 40 million. By 2019 it had passed 112 million (Figure 2).

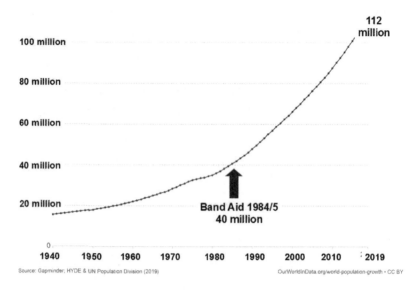

100 million

80 million

60 million

40 million

20 million

Band Aid 1984/5
40 million

112
million

0

1940 1950 1960 1970 1980 1990 2000 2010 2019

Source: Gapminder; HYDE & UN Population Division (2019)

OurWorldInData.org/world-population-growth · CC BY

Figure 2 – Population growth in Ethiopia

The populations of many other Third-World countries are on similar growth trajectories. Within ten years or less, using valuable arable land to produce fuel for vehicles in the rich West rather than for food for the world's poorest, may come to be seen as a moral obscenity.

There is one further problem with biofuels – massive deforestation. Brazil is one of the world's largest producers and users of biofuels. It produces over 30% of the world's biofuels. At 54% the U.S. produces more. Europe accounts for just 5%, China 3% and the rest of the world 8%. Currently, around 27% of all transport fuel used in Brazil is biofuels – mostly from sugar cane. Brazil's growing demand for biofuels is one of several reasons why large tracts of Amazon rainforests are being cut down and burned to make way for more farmland to produce more biofuels. And the destruction of the rainforests is reducing the acreage of trees which can absorb the CO_2 humans are adding to the atmosphere thus rendering the increasing use of biofuels in Brazil somewhat redundant.

Indonesia has often been criticised for cutting down its rainforests to make way for palm oil plantations. This environmental destruction has been blamed for the rapidly decreasing numbers of orangutangs and other species. Environmentalists have launched the occasional campaign against food and cosmetic companies for their supposed complicity in Indonesia's environmental vandalism. But around 65% of all the EU's imports of palm oil from Indonesia and Malaysia was used for biofuels. The environmental campaigners somehow don't seem so keen on mentioning that.

To be fair to environmental groups, some of the less rabid campaigners did start to realise that promoting biofuels had been a disastrous mistake. Environmental groups led by Greenpeace asked the EU Commission to drop its 10% target. A Friends of the Earth spokesperson said: 'I just can't see how the Commission can go ahead with its biofuels policy now.' But, ignoring the pleas of the more sensible environmentalists, the Commission did go ahead because, as the Commission explained: 'The planet is facing irreversible climate change unless action is taken quickly. The EU has already formulated a clear response in the shape of an integrated energy and climate change policy, a commitment to cut greenhouse gases by at least 20 percent by 2020.'

By 2020, the pressure to accept that their biofuels policy had resulted in huge environmental destruction pushed the EU into imposing limits on imports of products – palm oil, soy and maize – which were linked to deforestation. But the EU maintained its biofuels targets insisting that fuels made from deforestation crops be replaced by biofuels from crops like rapeseed and sunflowers as well as recycling waste oils. However, the EU Commission's decision didn't do anything to address the other two problems with biofuels – that their cultivation, production and use emits more CO_2 than equivalent amounts of fossil fuels and that arable land used to grow biofuels feedstock might be better employed growing food for the one third of the world's population which lacks food security.

Moreover, the EU's limits on palm oil imports will be unlikely to save the orangutans or any other wildlife threatened by deforestation. In 2018, the Indonesian government mandated the use of 20% biodiesel in cars and ships as well as in fields like construction. The required proportion of biofuel has since been raised to 30% and then to 40% by 2021. Moreover, work in Indonesia also has begun on D100, a biodiesel made entirely from palm oil. Palm oil supports so many jobs that the Indonesian government cannot risk harming the industry. Furthermore, like another major user of biofuels, Brazil, the Indonesian government hopes that home-grown biofuels can be used to reduce imports of fossil fuels and thus cut the country's trade deficit.

Biofuels release more CO_2 into the atmosphere than the fossil fuels they are meant to be replace to supposedly save the planet. Moreover, they have led to widespread deforestation, environmental destruction and threatened the survival of many animal species. In addition, by reducing the amount of arable land used for food production, they are the main cause of rising food prices which have blighted the lives of hundreds of millions of the world's poorest. But while the EU squirms and wriggles to find ways of keeping its commitments to biofuel use without trashing the Earth's forests, some countries, for reasons of their own, are hugely increasing their use of biofuels. Like so many policies designed to save the world from the non-existent threat of CAGW, the rush to biofuels by weak-minded, self-serving, short-termist, scientifically-ignorant politicians under pressure from well-organised, vociferous but equally scientifically-ignorant political activists seems to have had the opposite effect to what was intended.

LET THE WIND BLOW HIGH, LET THE WIND BLOW LOW[62]

Climate catastrophists try to convince us of the benefits of wind and solar power by claiming they provide electricity with absolutely no CO_2 emissions. Wind and solar power, we are repeatedly told, are just pure nature powering both our homes and all the wonderful, environmentally-friendly, and rather expensive, electric cars we're going to be forced to buy. And what could be more beneficial for our supposedly over-heating planet than this hundred percent natural energy?

This, of course, overlooks all the materials required to build wind turbines and solar panels. There are many different estimates of the amount of materials used to build and install wind turbines. And obviously the amounts used depend on the size of the turbine. But just as a guide, we could take the figures produced by the U.S. Geological Survey.[63] According to these, a large wind turbine with a theoretical capacity of five megawatts (enough to power about 2,000 homes) would need at least 500 tonnes of steel, 2,000 tonnes of concrete, 30 tonnes of fibreglass, 15 tonnes of copper and 20 tonnes of cast iron. Another source calculated that the manufacture of this material emitted over 240 tonnes of CO_2. Whether these figures are scientifically-accurate or just swags, they do at least indicate that wind turbines are far from being the zero-emitters providing natural CO_2-free energy that the climate catastrophists claim.

Then, of course, you need conventional fossil-fuel back-up to provide power for those times when the wind speed is less than about 8 mph (13 km/h). Also, when the wind is more than around 55 mph (88 km/h) back-up is also needed as turbines will shut down at high wind speeds to avoid being damaged. This duplication of energy production facilities for wind-free and stormy days tends not to be mentioned by those promoting the environmental benefits of wind power.

Wind-power enthusiasts often highlight the theoretical capacity of wind turbines – what's called the 'nameplate capacity'. But this nameplate capacity is usually based on the wind blowing at an ideal speed 24 hours a day, 365 days a year. Of course, this has never happened and never will. Studies done so far suggest that the average onshore wind turbine will deliver somewhere around 24% of its theoretical capacity. Due to slightly more reliable wind at sea than on land, perhaps offshore turbines can achieve up to 35% of theoretical capacity. Though, due to the harsher environment for offshore wind turbines, they probably lose more output than onshore turbines due to requiring more frequent maintenance shutdowns. So we should take claims of millions of homes being CO_2-cleanly powered by the wind with more than a little care. And we should check whether, when promoting the benefits of wind, the windophiliacs are talking about 'nameplate capacity' or actual, realistic output?

WE NEED TO BUILD MORE LAND

But the biggest, and often seldom-mentioned, drawback of wind power is the vast amount of land required to produce often quite modest amounts of electricity. There are many ways of estimating how much land will be needed for wind turbines to meet our political leaders', climate activists' and school-children's plans for our net-zero nirvana by 2050.

A study done by Princeton University in 2020/2021 calculated that, for the U.S. to supply half of its predicted 2050 energy use from wind and a third from solar, would require 210,000 square miles (544,000 km²) to be covered by wind farms and a further 15,000 square miles (39,000 km²) devoted to solar.[64] That's equivalent to using around 7.5% of all USA land for wind turbines and solar farms.

The UK government's plans issued in December 2020, are curiously similar to the Princeton University's energy projections for the U.S.. The UK Department for Business, Energy and Industrial Strategy has modelled the UK's energy future based on 50% of our 2050 energy coming from wind and 33% from solar –

very close to the Princeton estimates for the U.S. The UK government also plans for two thirds of the country's 2050 wind energy coming from offshore turbines and the rest from onshore wind farms.

Assuming an energy density of around 2 W/m² for offshore wind and 1.5 W/m² for onshore wind, the UK would need about 23,000 square miles (60,000 km²) of shallow coastal waters and around 15,000 square miles (40,000 km²) – over 16% of the UK's total land area – for onshore wind farms to meet the UK government's admirable wind-power ambitions.

You may argue with these calculations. But they should at least help demonstrate the likely amount of land needed for the planned wind-power electricity. They thus suggest that the climate catastrophists and sycophantic, gravy-train-riding scientists encouraging the politicians in their fantasies of a net-zero world powered half by wind have long since lost all sense of the impossibility of ever implementing their planet-saving dreams.

In what can only be described as a total absurdity, at the same time as Western governments are encouraging the planting of millions more trees to absorb CO2 from the atmosphere to help get their countries to net zero, they're cutting down millions of trees to make way for more wind turbines. This is happening in Scotland where a 'mere' 14 million trees have reportedly been slaughtered so far:

The Herald

NEWS

28th February 2020

14m trees have been cut down in Scotland to make way for wind farms

By David Bol | @mrdavidbol
Political Correspondent

21 wind farms have been constructed on forestry land

🄵 🅣 🄸🄽 ✉ 🗩 91 comments

NEARLY 14 million trees have been chopped down across Scotland to make way for wind turbines.

And in Germany, thousands of acres of ancient forests are being razed to create space for the country's growing wind turbine population.

Of course, wind technology will improve and the power output of wind turbines will increase. But on the other hand, the more wind farms there are, the more will have to be built in areas with lower wind strengths. So, it's not obvious that improving technology will compensate for wind farms being built in ever less wind-rich areas. If you then factor in that a wind turbine might, with good maintenance, last 15 years (the windophiliacs claim it's 25 years), whereas a gas-fired power station should have an operating life of 30 years or more, not only will you be carpet bombing the UK with massive and ugly wind turbines, but you'll also have to replace them at huge expense much faster than equivalent fossil-fuel power stations.

In addition to the vast amount of land required for wind turbines, you also have to factor in that they cannot be built within 700 metres of any homes due to the infrasound the turbines emit. According to Google: 'Reported effects include those on the inner ear, vertigo, imbalance, etc.; intolerable sensations, incapacitation, disorientation, nausea, vomiting, and bowel spasm; and resonances in inner organs, such as the heart. Infrasound has also been observed to affect the pattern of sleep minutely.'

Moreover, let's not forget the bird-chomping. It has been estimated that even at today's relatively low wind-power use, over 100,000 birds are killed each year by wind turbines. By 2050 there will be around eight times as many wind turbines in and around the UK. So it would not be unreasonable to suspect the avian death toll to reach close to a million birds a year. Though, as the Royal Society for the Protection of Birds estimates that the UK's 8 to 10 million domestic cats slaughter up to 100 million prey every year, including around 27 million birds, if we really want to save nature and our birdlife, perhaps we should sterilise all our cats and all work towards a wonderful cat-zero 2050?

The bottom line with our government's wind-power ambitions is that the UK had better start building an awful lot more land and shallow coastline very fast if it is going to find room to fit in all the wind turbines planned to supply half of the UK's electricity by 2050 as part of the UK government's 'ambitious' 2050 net-zero target.

GROWING PINEAPPLES IN ALASKA?

Solar power does have one advantage over wind – its energy density is greater than wind, so solar requires less land for the same power output as wind. The world's largest solar farm is Bhadla Solar Park in India. Officially recognized as a sandy, dry, and arid region Bhadla is located about 200 km (120 miles) north of Jodhpur and about 320 km (200 miles) west of the state capital Jaipur. The region has been described as "almost unliveable" due its climate. Average temperatures in Bhadla hover between 46°C and 48°C (115°F and 118°F), with hot winds and sand storms occurring frequently.

Bhadla Solar Park produces about 6 W/m² and has over 2,700 hours of strong sunshine each year. London has around, 1,573 hours of weak sunshine a year, Paris 1,660 and Berlin 1,650. So, solar energy installations in rainy, often overcast soon-to-be-net-zero Europe will be considerably less productive than the 6 W/m² achieved in scorching Bhadla. Although those touting the benefits of solar energy cite figures of between 5 W/m² to 9 W/m² from European solar parks, judging from what Bhadla produces, perhaps about 3 W/m² would be the realistic maximum for a Northern European solar park?

The UK plans to produce as much as 120 gigawatts of electricity from solar by 2050 – up from about 13 gigawatts today. Using an assumed energy density of 3 W/m² for solar farms in the UK, this would mean more than another 15,000 square miles (40,000 km²) of the UK being covered by solar farms. With 15,000 square miles of the UK land area beautified by onshore wind turbines and another 15,000 square miles decorated by attractive solar panels, around a third of the small, already overcrowded UK's 93,640 square miles (242,500 km²) land area would have to be used to enable the country to meet its net zero targets by 2050.

Hopefully, someone senior in the British Civil Service with their reputed 'Rolls Royce' brains has worked this out and explained it to our net-zero-fixated political leaders as they grandstand with ever more ambitious CO_2-reduction delusions?

When asked about his company's plans for solar power, the Chief Executive of one of Germany's largest energy producers said that producing solar power in Germany is: 'as sensible as growing pineapples in Alaska.'

RENEWABLES ARE REALLY CHEAP. NOT!

There were some excited headlines in the climate alarmist media in 2019 and 2020:

'Renewable energy is now the cheapest option,'

— *Forbes*, 15 June 2019

Wind and solar plants will soon be cheaper than coal in all big markets around world, analysis finds,'

— *The Guardian*, 12 March 2020

'Renewables beat even cheapest coal,'

— International Renewable Energy Agency (IRENA) 2 June 2020

If these headlines were true, the basic principles of capitalism would suggest that there should be no need for our governments to shower commercial energy companies with massive subsidies to replace fossil-fuel energy generation with these supposedly much cheaper renewables. And we'd all be shunning fossil-fuel energy in favour of renewables to lower our energy bills. However, the countries with the highest electricity prices, like Germany and Denmark, tend to be those with the highest percentage of renewable energy generation. This suggests that renewables may not be quite as cheap as the eco-warriors like to suggest. So, it might be worth examining a little further the claims that renewables are cheaper than fossil-fuel alternatives.

If we look at the U.S., onshore wind at $39 per megawatt and solar at $44 per megawatt clearly appear to be cheaper than coal, gas, nuclear and offshore wind (Figure 4).[65]

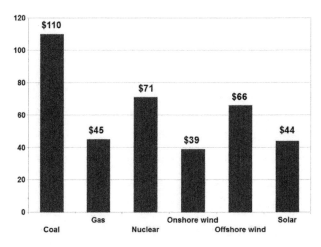

Figure 4 – U.S. Energy costs of generating electricity ($/MWh 2019/2020)

The same is true for Europe with onshore wind at $55 per megawatt and solar at $70 per megawatt (Figure 5).

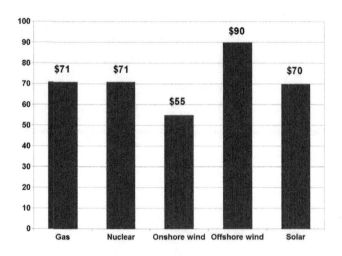

Figure 5 – Europe Energy costs of generating electricity ($/MWh 2019/2020)

But I believe that these prices don't include a critical difference between renewables and their fossil-fuel competitors. Fossil fuels and nuclear can provide constant electricity 24 hours a day 365 days a year whatever the weather. Solar and wind are intermittent, unreliable, unpredictable and require expensive fossil-fuel back-up to be available for those times when there is too little or too much wind or when there is insufficient sun. For example, the heaviest time for domestic electricity usage in industrialised Northern Europe is probably during the winter months when people come home from work and expect to cook their meals and take baths and showers in centrally-heated homes (Figure 6).

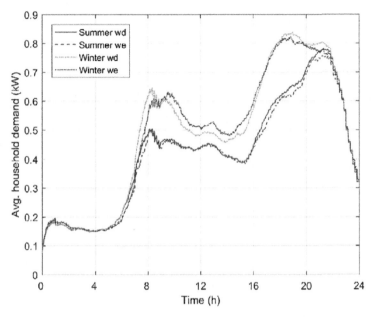

Figure 6 – Average UK domestic energy use by time of day[66]

Yet the time when most electricity is needed is precisely the time when there isn't too much sun – ergo, solar electricity is pretty useless. So homes will have to be powered by wind (if there is any) and fossil-fuel back-up. Of course, you could argue that industrial energy users will reach their peak demand during the day when there is the most sun. But by the time the West's energy prices reach eight to ten times energy prices of countries like China, India, Vietnam and Thailand, there won't be too much industry left in the West to use the glorious midday solar power.

We therefore need to be more than slightly careful when the greenwashing climate catastrophists try to convince us that renewable energy is admirably cheap. It isn't.

NEW TECHNOLOGIES

Within maybe ten to twenty years, real scientists may have developed new technologies to provide us with better, more reliable and even cheaper energy. Possible new energy sources could include molten salt reactors, green hydrogen, wave energy converters, and many more we probably don't know about yet. One day these may largely replace fossil fuels in richer countries. Though developing countries may still have to rely on coal and natural gas for their electricity. But there is one certainty – today's supposed 'renewables' may provide part of our energy needs, but they are too expensive, too unreliable, too land-intensive, far too environmentally-damaging and too inconsistent to be taken seriously as our major energy source. If our rulers really want to go down the renewables route, they should take the precaution of mothballing conventional power stations so these can be brought back into service if renewables prove as useless as many climate realists believe. Unfortunately our leaders, terrified by screaming climate catastrophists, are tearing down fossil-fuel power stations apparently forgetting that burning bridges behind oneself is not a particularly great idea when one might be forced to retreat in a hurry in the future.

CHAPTER 15

How did we let it happen?

This is probably the most difficult chapter to write. After all, when tens of millions of people believe, often fanatically, in something that is a delusion with little to no scientific basis, to even suggest that these tens of millions are misguided can make one look like a crazed, tin-foil-hat wearing conspiracy theorist. In a madhouse, it's the sane person who is judged to be mad.

One approach may be to try to look at the different possible causes of the catastrophic anthropogenic global warming psychosis. These causes can probably be split into three main areas – the (mis)information we are being fed; the current state of Western society and human behaviour.

The information, or more accurately 'misinformation', we are being fed includes the dishonesty and politicisation of the IPCC (Intergovernmental Panel on Climate Change) and the extraordinary bias of the mainstream media's reporting of anything to do with the climate.

The current state of Western society refers to the dumbing down of our education systems; the West's narcissistic oikophobia; the rise of the free-speech-loathing woke; and democracy being supplanted by kakistocracy and technocracy.

Human behaviour describes our tendency towards anthropocentrism and people's need for a great moral cause to reinforce their own perception of their high ethical standards and give meaning to their lives.

THE IPCC AND THE POLITICISATION OF SCIENCE

Most people probably believe that they can trust the reports by the Nobel-Prize-winning IPCC. But when you look at the terms of reference for the IPCC, you can already see that it is biased towards only one conclusion. The IPCC's own website explains that the IPCC was set up:

> 'to assess on a comprehensive, objective, open and transparent basis the scientific, technical and socio-economic information relevant to understanding the scientific basis of risk of human-induced climate change, its potential impacts and options for adaptation and mitigation.'

There are several problems with this. The key one is that the IPCC assumes that climate change is 'human-induced'. There is no attempt to analyse the possible causes of climate change – natural temperature variation, effects of being in an interglacial, changes in solar activity, planetary orbit and tilt, cloud cover and water vapour, ocean current cycles and so on – and to assess whether human activities are a major or minor contributor to changes in climate or not even a contributor at all.

This is almost similar to a police investigation being launched to establish how often you beat your wife or husband or partner or dog or cat or hamster or whatever. There is no attempt to establish whether you beat them or not. That you do beat them is taken for granted. The investigation is therefore only aimed at finding out how often you beat them and how hard you beat them. Likewise, the IPCC takes it for granted that humans are causing climate change. Their mission is thus to establish how seriously humans are affecting the climate.

Moreover, the IPCC has the words 'objective' and 'scientific' in its charter. Given that the IPCC has already decided that humans are responsible for climate change, it cannot consider any scientific evidence or articles that dispute the assumption of humans' guilt. So the IPCC cannot be 'objective' or 'scientific'. It has already been hijacked from the start by those who want to force through their beliefs that humans are the main cause of climate change.

In addition, the IPCC is tasked with looking at: 'options for adaptation and mitigation.' This automatically assumes that climate change is so serious that we must try to adapt to it and/or mitigate it. Yet there is no scientific evidence that climate change is a particularly serious problem. If anything, the evidence suggests that the last fifty or so years have been remarkably good for the human race. We've had fewer storms, fewer hurricanes, fewer droughts, fewer forest fires, fewer floods. Plus we've had the added benefits of the Earth greening and crop yields increasing.

There have been many other criticisms of the work of the IPCC. Possibly the best analysis of these is in Christopher Booker's 2009 book *The Real Global Warming Disaster*. These criticisms have mainly centered on there being too many climate activists with no published, peer-reviewed papers being invited as contributors and even as editors; scientists who have expressed doubts about the theory of catastrophic anthropogenic global warming being excluded from all IPCC work; the *Summary for Policymakers* (the only bit of the hundreds of pages of IPCC reports that journalists and politicians ever look at) ignoring the views of qualified contributors in order to include exaggerated and unsubstantiated claims about the certainties of climate change being caused by human activities; and the deliberate manipulation of data to support the CAGW agenda.

Several leading scientists have even risked their careers by resigning in disgust at the misinformation put out by the IPCC and the politicisation of its work to support the CAGW message.

One of the world's experts on cyclones and hurricanes wrote in his resignation letter:

'I am withdrawing because I have come to view the part of the IPCC to which my expertise is relevant as having become politicized. In addition, when I have raised my concerns to the IPCC leadership, their response was simply to dismiss my concerns.' He added 'All previous and current research in the area of hurricane variability has shown no reliable, long-term trend up in the frequency or intensity of tropical cyclones, either in the Atlantic or any other basin . . . It is beyond me why my colleagues would utilize the media to push an unsupported agenda that recent hurricane activity has been due to global warming.' The letter concluded: 'I personally cannot in good faith continue to contribute to a process that I view as both being motivated by pre-conceived agendas and being scientifically unsound.'

A leading authority on tropical diseases gave evidence to a U.S. Senate committee in which he said:

'A galling aspect of the debate is that this spurious 'science' is endorsed in the public forum by influential panels of "experts." I refer particularly to the Intergovernmental Panel on Climate Change (IPCC). Every five years, this UN-based organization publishes a 'consensus of the world's top scientists' on all aspects of climate change. Quite apart from the dubious process by which these scientists are selected, such consensus is the stuff of politics, not of science.'

Furthermore, in a report to the UK House of Lords he wrote:

'In my opinion, the IPCC has done a disservice to society by relying on "experts" who have little or no knowledge of the subject, and allowing them to make authoritative pronounce-ments that are not based on sound science.'

THE MEDIA BECOME CLIMATE PROPAGANDISTS

A strange feature of Western mainstream media is that, the more access we all have to information from the Internet, the more our mainstream media seem to have given up any pretence of providing unbiased news. Instead, the media have increasingly become just mouth-frothing propagandists for particular political and social views. Journalists and interviewers repeatedly fawn obsequiously over anyone who shares their views, while treating anyone who might disagree even mildly with those views with sneering contempt and seething hostility.

In the U.S., the barrage of continual abuse with which most U.S. media treated President Trump for over four years, while lying about Trump's supposed Russian collusion connections was sickening to any unbiased observer. Moreover, during the 2020 presidential campaign, the U.S. media's attempts to destroy Trump while eulogising his clearly physically- and mentally-declining presidential rival, Joe Biden, looked more like a satire than real life.

There was a similar situation in the UK where anyone who dared admit they supported leaving the European Union was portrayed by the media as poorly-educated, ignorant, racist and xenophobic. Moreover, the media did all they could to flatter the views of Europhiliacs, while as much as possible denigrating or simply censoring Brexiteers. No attempt was ever made at providing balanced reporting of the Brexit debate. Nor did it seem to occur to anyone in the mainstream media that there should be a balanced debate at all.

This tendency for the media propagandising, instead of reporting facts, has been clearly displayed with supposed CAGW. Any scientist making claims about the alleged ghastly consequences of man-made warming, however ludicrously exaggerated and unfounded those claims, is invariably treated as a farsighted genius. For example, in spite of sea levels possibly rising by just a few millimetres a decade, scientists appeared in TV documentaries and press interviews predicting a four- to six-foot rise sea-level rise within the next 80 years without ever being challenged by journalists over their preposterous predictions. No climate realists were ever invited on the documentaries to provide some sanity and balance.

Even when the UK's former chief scientific adviser insisted that Antarctica, which currently has a temperature of around –57°C (–70.6°F) and is adding billions of tons of new ice every year, would be the only habitable continent by the end of this century, this was faithfully reported by the media as being the utterances of a great, knowledgable climate oracle:

THE INDEPENDENT **ENVIRONMENT**

Why Antarctica will soon be the *only* place to live - literally

By Geoffrey Lean, Environment Editor

Sunday, 2 May 2004

Antarctica is likely to be the world's only habitable continent by the end of this century if global warming remains unchecked, the Government's chief scientist, Professor Sir David King, said last week.

Not a single journalist or interviewer thought to ask, if global temperatures are now rising at perhaps an almost imperceptible 0.6°C to 0.8°C every hundred years, how they were going to shoot up by well over 50°C in the rest of this century to melt the

2–3 kilometre thick Antarctic ice sheet to make Antarctica the habitable paradise that the UK's former chief scientific adviser foresaw. Even worse, when the Chinese Wuhan plague hit the UK, one of the people most interviewed on TV for his extensive scientific knowledge was none other than the man who predicted we'd all have to go and live in Antarctica by the end of the 21st Century.

Then there was the infamous '97% of scientists agree CAGW is happening' claim. In Chapter 9, I tried to show that this claim was utter and total nonsense. Given how often our rulers have used the '97% of scientists' claim to bludgeon us into accepting ever more restrictions on our freedoms and ever more taxes on our lives to supposedly save the planet, it's beyond incredible that not a single investigative journalist and not a single mainstream media editor has shown the slightest interest in exposing the '97% of scientists' lie.

Perhaps even more shameful than the shenanigans used by the biased and politicised IPCC to browbeat our leaders and us into terrified obedience to their increasingly demented demands on us to sacrifice the benefits of an advanced industrialised civilisation based on constant, cheap energy mainly from fossil fuels, has been the behaviour of the mainstream media in propagandising the increasingly discredited CAGW cult.

WHY DO WE HATE OURSELVES? OIKOPHOBIA

Western society – including Europe, the U.S., Australia and New Zealand – like all societies has its faults. Nevertheless, it's probably the greatest society the human race has produced in terms of sharing of wealth, looking after the more vulnerable, providing justice and legal protections for its citizens, its scientific and artistic achievements and its medical progress. Yet there are large groups of people living in the West, and benefiting from the freedoms, access to education and healthcare and relative affluence the West offers, who seem to hate the countries in which they live and who delight in reviling everything about the West – both the current state of Western society and the West's history.

There is a word 'oikophobia' believed to have been coined by the British philosopher, Roger Scruton, in his 2004 book *England and the Need for Nations*. Oikophobia comes from the Greek oîkos – 'house, household' and phóbos – 'fear'. One definition of oikophobia is a 'hatred of one's country or compatriots' or 'the felt need to denigrate the customs, culture and institutions that are identifiably those of your own country.'

The theory behind oikophobia is that it is nothing new. Instead it's a natural phase in the decline of many civilisations. Each civilisation starts to form. Initial successes against other peoples allow it to grow becoming more powerful and wealthier and a sense of shared identity is forged. With success, each civilisation creates a leisure class and even those lower on the social scale can work to advance themselves towards having at least some of the accoutrements of the wealthier leisure classes.

At the zenith of its success, each civilisation starts to believe that it is invincible and therefore not under any existential threat from external forces or peoples. Rather than enjoying the achievements of that civilisation, some groups within it turn on each other in what Freud has called the 'narcissism of small differences'. Then that civilisation starts disintegrating into largely trivial, but increasingly poisonous, internal squabbles in which there is at first mutual incomprehension and then mutual loathing between the warring cultural tribes who try to impose their beliefs on everyone else. The current intemperate furore over whether trans men can be real women and trans women can be real men is a perfect example of this self-destructive madness.

Finally that civilisation can no longer project an effective, unified outward force and disintegrates allowing a rival to take its place. We can clearly see that, while the 20th Century was dominated by the West, the West is now tearing itself apart in its internal culture wars in the 21st Century allowing an increasingly expansionist and aggressive China to become the dominant force in the world. Part of the West's oikophobia is the misguided determination of climate catastrophists, the media and political leaders to see the advanced West as an evil force wrecking the planet. Their sense of self-hatred is causing them to force us to commit economic and societal suicide by replacing the cheap, reliable and abundant fossil fuels, which have powered the West's ascendancy, with expensive, unreliable, intermittent, environment-destroying supposed 'renewables'.

THE RISE OF POLITICAL INCOMPETENCE? KAKISTOCRACY

Here's another word derived from Greek – Kakistocracy. The word is formed from two Greek words: *kakistos* – worst and *kratos* – rule. It means a government that is run by the worst, least qualified, and/or most unscrupulous citizens.

Up till the latter part of the 20th Century, the West had leaders who had either endured the horrors of WWII or who had been brought up in its shadows – John F. Kennedy, Ronald Reagan, Helmut Kohl, François Mitterand, George Bush senior, Margaret Thatcher. You might not have agreed with their politics. But most people would probably accept that all these leaders were driven by a clear sense of moral purpose. But now we have a new generation of professional politicians – in the U.S. there were the Clintons. In Britain there was possibly the greatest actor of his generation – Antony Charles Lynton Blair. These politicians spent most of their lives in a political bubble where the keys to success were not strong beliefs or managerial effectiveness. Instead attributes like sycophancy, chameleon-like adaptability to whichever way the wind was blowing and playing internal party politics were the way to self-advancement and self-enrichment.

Today's leaders are mostly in politics for their own self-aggrandizement, for the pleasure of being surrounded by fawning flunkies and for the financial rewards they could never achieve in any other field. Without any strong moral compass, these leaders gave us focus-group policies. They pandered to whatever they thought would improve their popularity, electability and power. They gave us kakistocracy – governments of the most unscrupulous and the least competent.

None of them have had the courage to stand up to the laughably exaggerated and palpably dishonest doom-mongering by the climate catastrophists. None of them have dared question the increasingly discredited climate disaster forecasts. None of them have even attempted to understand the science of the Earth's climate. Instead our leaders have grovelled to the preachers of climate catastrophe and are leading us to economic and societal collapse. But why should they worry? By the time people realise what has happened, our leaders will all have long since retired to live out the rest of their pampered, multi-millionaire lives in a level of comfort most of us could only dream of, while the rest of us and our children and their children will have to pay for our incompetent, self-serving rulers' intellectual stupidity and moral cowardice.

FROM KAKISTOCRACY TO TECHNOCRACY?

Moreover, having spent their lives with others of their kind and having mostly never had a proper job, today's leaders, whatever their political party, have more in common with each other than they do with those who elect them. In fact, many politicians despise concepts like patriotism and sense of community and have nothing but contempt for ordinary voters and even their own countries. Instead, our rulers prefer to hand over power to organisations run by international technocrats rather than trusting their own domestic parliaments.

In Europe, this abrogation of political power and responsibility had disastrous consequences when 27 EU countries handed over procurement of vaccines against the Chinese Wuhan plague to the incompetent, unelected EU Commission made up of mostly failed politicians and bureaucrats. Recidivist bungling by the Commission and its bureaucrats resulted in the EU's vaccination campaign wasting at least two months. At the height of the Chinese plague, the EU politicians and bureaucrats even took two- to three-week Christmas and New Year holidays when they should have been working on accelerating vaccine approvals and procurement. It never occurred to the EU politicians and technocrats that saving the lives of EU citizens might be more important than their holidays. Meanwhile increasing numbers of EU citizens were catching Covid-19. At the worst period of the Chinese plague, over 30,000 EU citizens were dying every week (Figure 1).

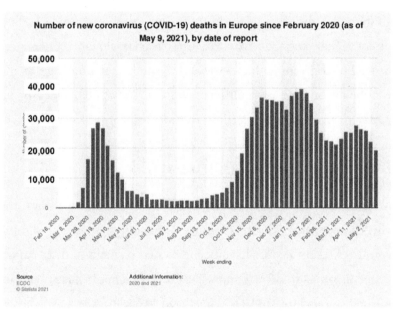

Figure 1 – Weekly EU27 death rates from Covid-19

If we take the deaths figure of 30,000 a week at the worst period of the Chinese Wuhan flu and assume a third of these lives could have been saved if vaccination had started two months earlier, then that gives around 80,000 EU citizens' lives which were lost because EU country leaders preferred to defend the supposedly inviolable sanctity of the 'EU project' rather than the lives of their own citizens.

Now we see a similar disaster being played out on a much larger scale as Western leaders hand over responsibility for their energy policy, and thus the economic futures of their countries, to the dubious scientists, anti-capitalist activists and probably incompetent technocrats of the UN's Intergovernmental Panel on Climate Change. Our rulers would rather grandstand and preen and strut and make absurd promises to garner the approval of their international peers at massive international climate conferences instead of concerning themselves with mundane matters such as the well-being of their own citizens. We truly have democracy being replaced by kakistocracy leading to the worst form of technocracy.

DUMBING DOWN OUR CHILDREN?

Much has been written in many Western countries about the alleged dumbing down of our education systems. In some countries, exam boards have been accused of making their papers easier in order to attract more customers. Schools have allegedly pushed pupils into subjects considered as 'easier' and have chosen the most 'friendly' exam boards in order to improve their results. And some subjects, such as mathematics, have been declared as subconsciously racist because they supposedly discriminate against and thus disadvantage people from less affluent backgrounds. Rather than get into a 'he said – she said' argument here between those who claim education is being dumbed down and those who maintain it is better than ever, I propose to look at possibly the most objective assessment of our schools' performance – the PISA survey – in just five Western countries.

The PISA study (Programme for International Student Assessment) is a worldwide study by the Organisation for Economic Co-operation and Development (OECD) in member and non-member nations intended to evaluate educational systems by measuring 15-year-old school pupils' scholastic performance in mathematics, science, and reading. It assesses over 500,000 school pupils. It was first performed in 2000 and then repeated every three years. Its aim is to provide comparable data with a view to enabling countries to improve their education policies and outcomes. It measures problem-solving and cognition. Figure 2 shows the PISA rankings for the U.S., UK, Australia, Germany and France in Science and Mathematics for the years 2000, 2012 and 2018. The nearer it is to 'I', the better that country's educational performance.

	Science			Maths		
	2000	2012	2018	2000	2012	2018
USA	15	28	18	20	36	37
UK	5	20	14	9	26	17
Australia	8	16	15	6	19	29
Germany	21	12	15	21	16	20
France	13	26	24	11	25	25

Figure 2 – PISA rankings 2000 – 2012 – 2018

In science, four of the five countries – USA, UK, Australia and France – have fallen significantly between 2000 and 2018. Germany has improved slightly, but started off lower than the other four countries. In maths the results are nothing short of shameful. The same four countries – have fallen even more dismally low in the international rankings. Germany was already the lowest performer of the five countries in 2000 and has remained pretty stagnant.

The results for reading are fairly similar – these five key Western countries have continued to fall behind their international competitors in their levels of educational achievement. This is not the place to discuss why this has happened. But the results should speak for themselves – a clear failure by the education systems in the five countries in Figure 2 to equip their children with abilities to understand and solve problems. It is hardly surprising that children with only a most basic grasp of science and betrayed by the failing education systems in these five countries are so easily convinced by the purveyors of the catastrophic anthropogenic global warming dogma.

A PERFECT STORM?

We seem to have a perfect storm.

There is an international organisation – the IPCC – whose terms of reference prevented it ever being genuinely unbiased and objectively scientific. The IPCC has banned any scientists who dare question its CAGW theory and has become increasingly hijacked by climate activists and, often capitalism-loathing, ideologues intent on imposing their de-industrialisation policies on the advanced West in pursuit of some Rousseau-istic vision of the purity of a more natural lifestyle.

Moreover, any announcement from the IPCC or any CAGW-proselytising scientist or self-proclaimed scientist, however exaggerated and/or absurd, is treated by the biased, craven media as irrefutable truth because the media hide behind the claim 'the science is settled' even though the science of understanding a highly complex thermodynamic system like the Earth's climate will probably never be fully settled.

Added to this we have a self-destructive oikophobia in large sections of Western society and a continual bombardment in the media from people who hate our society, our freedoms, our institutions and especially our success compared to large parts of the world. For the oikophobes, imposing net zero gives them the chance to destroy a political and economic system they loathe. We are further weakened because few, if any, of our political leaders are motivated by any clear moral code and few have gained power by showing any managerial competence in any field outside of politics. Moreover, they have much more in common with their international peers than the people who voted for them and have more allegiance to multi-national organisations like the EU, UN and the UN's IPCC than to the countries they govern.

Then you can throw into the mix a generation of children who are being brainwashed with progressive, woke propaganda in failing education systems which no longer try to teach children to think for themselves. Add a tendency of humans towards anthropocentrism – a narcissistic belief that everything that happens revolves around us humans. And spice this up with the human need for a great moral cause to reinforce our self-image of superiority over others and to give meaning to our lives. After all, what moral cause could be greater than saving humanity and the planet from extinction? It's no wonder that the Extinction Rebellion activists get such moral masturbatory pleasure from their tedious, disruptive and pointless protests.

Put all this together and you have a perfect storm which has allowed the catastrophic anthropogenic climate change delusion to dominate our lives.

This chapter is far from being an in-depth study of the extraordinary spread of the CAGW psychosis. But it hopefully gives some indications as to how the West became obsessed with a fantasy which has no scientific basis, which is continually disproved by the failure of its models and its predictions and which is leading the West to its own wilful economic and societal self-immolation while the rest of the world licks its lips at the spoils to be had from our self-deluded suicide.

To quote one of the world's leading real climate scientists and a vociferous critic of the IPCC circus:

'What historians will definitely wonder about in future centuries is how deeply flawed logic, obscured by shrewd and unrelenting propaganda, actually enabled a coalition of powerful special interests to convince nearly everyone in the world that CO_2 from human industry was a dangerous, planet-destroying toxin. It will be remembered as the greatest mass delusion in the history of the world – that CO2, the life of plants, was considered for a time to be a deadly poison.'

What about the supposed 'scientists' and journalists who have been bombarding us with CAGW propaganda for the last 30 to 40 years? After the real catastrophe of the Chinese Wuhan plague, does anyone believe anything the scientific and media elites tell us any more? We knew right at the start of the Chinese Covid-19 plague:

– The French scientists who helped design and build the biosafety level-4 Wuhan Institute of Virology were prevented by the Chinese authorities from overseeing the work there

– U.S. diplomats who visited the Wuhan Institute of Virology in 2018 sent urgent messages to the U.S. State Department warning about slovenly hygiene practices and the dangers of a deadly virus being released by accident

– American virologists had taught the key scientists at Wuhan how to do 'gain of function' research on bat viruses

– The Institute had collected more than 2,000 bat viruses for experimentation

– Virologists in Wuhan were using biosafety level-2 labs, a bit like your local vet's clinic, for research on deadly pathogens

– Gain of function research had been stopped in the U.S. due to the dangers of a leak, but it continued at Wuhan

In spite of all of this, when the then president, Donald Trump, and his Secretary of State, Mike Pompeo, suggested that the Chinese Covid-19 plague might have accidentally been released from a Wuhan lab, the scientific community and the mainstream media immediately leapt into action branding anyone mentioning the lab leak theory as crazed conspiracy theorists and as science-deniers. And the higher the Covid-19 death toll rose, the more frantic were the scientists and media to discredit those daring to suggest the obvious.

At the time of writing, the public have started to see through the scientists' and media's year of lying. So the scientists and media are desperately trying to throw up a smokescreen over their previous attempts to suppress the lab leak story and are now claiming that new information makes the lab leak theory 'plausible' and 'feasible'. Yet for most ordinary people the lab leak theory is blindingly obviously what really happened and many of us suspected this right from the start.

The self-serving, politicised, truth-perverting scientists and media have been totally discredited by their year of lying dangerously about the real source of the Wuhan Chinese Covid-19 plague. Perhaps people will now start to wonder whether the scientific and media elites might also have been lying to us about supposed catastrophic anthropogenic global warming? We can but hope.

Endnotes

1 The *Great Bend Tribune* 2 November 1922

2 *National Geographic* November 1976

3 *Observer* 11 November 2004

4 Observer 11 November 2004

5 *Newsweek* April 28 1975 The Cooling World

6 *New York Times* 18 July 1970

7 *Guardian* 10 August 2020

8 Lewis Gordon Pugh (May 2010). "Achieving the Impossible. A Fearless Leader. A Fragile Earth". Simon & Schuster

9 *Newcastle Morning Herald* 18 February 1952

10 Rutgers University Global Snow Laboratory

11 *The Mythology of Global Warming* Bruce C. Bunker Moonshine Cove Publishing 2018

12 https://www.earthmagazine.org/article/did-medieval-warm-period-welcome-vikings-greenland

13 *Greenland ice sheet mass balance reconstruction 1600 to 2009* Jason E. Box et al

14 *False Alarm* Bjorn Lomborg Basic Books 2020

15 *The polar bear catastrophe that never happened* Susan J. Crockford GWPF 2019

16 Wood Hole Oceanographic Institution 19 December 2018

17 CC BY-SA 3.0, https://commons.wikimedia.org/w/index.php?curid=479979

18 http://en.wikipedia.org/wiki/File:Recent_Sea_Level_Rise.png

19 By NASA – https://climate.nasa.gov/vital-signs/sea-level/, Public Domain, https://commons.wikimedia.org/w/index.php?curid=71578292

20 Australian *Daily Mail* 11 November 2019

21 *Daily Mail* 5 March 2015

22 Proxy climatic and environmental changes of the past 1,000 years Soon and Baliunas

23 *The Real Global Warming Disaster* Christopher Booker Continuum 2009

24 http://berkeleyearth.org/understanding-adjustments-temperature-data/

25 https://iopscience.iop.org/1748-9326/8/2/024024/media/erl460291datafile.txt

26 The Manhattan Declaration on Climate Change Tom Harris http://www.climatescienceinternational.org/index.php?option=com_content&task=view&id=37&

27 https://scied.ucar.edu/learning-zone/air-quality/whats-in-the-air

28 https://www.pnas.org/content/104/39/15248

29 *Time and frequency analysis of Vostok ice core climate data* Periodicals of Engineering and natural sciences ISSN 2303-4521 2 August 2019 pp 907-923

30 https://www.researchgate.net/figure/Global-Temperature-and-CO2-levels-over-600-million-years-Source-MacRae-2008_fig1_280548391

31 https://www.climate.gov/news-features/climate-qa/whats-hottest-earths-ever-been

32 *The Real Global Warming Disaster* Christopher Booker Continuum 2009

33 *Finance and Development* William R. Cline March 2008

34 *The Journal.ie* 8 June 2014

35 The *Barents Observer* 7 February 2020

36 *Greening of the Earth and its drivers* Nature Climate Change 25 April 2016

37 *Inconvenient Facts* Gregory Wrightstone Silver Crown Productions 2020

38 *The Conversation* 20 January 2021

39 Scientific Assessment Fifth session of the IPCC

40 *Soon*, W., and Yaskell, S.H., The Maunder Minimum and the Variable Sun-earth Connection (World Scientific Press: 2003) pp 87-88

41 CC BY-SA 3.0, https://commons.wikimedia.org/w/index.php?curid=969067

42 *The Real Inconvenient Truth* M.J. Sangster 2018

43 https://skepticalscience.com/solar-activity-sunspots-global-warming.htm

44 https://www.universetoday.com/39012/milankovitch-cycle/

45 https://i2.wp.com/timescavengers.blog/wp-content/uploads/2017/01/milankovitch-cycles.jpg?ssl=1

46 *The Real Inconvenient Truth* M.J. Sangster 2018

47 *Modulation of Ice Ages via Precession and Dust-Albedo Feedbacks* Ralph Ellis and Michael Palmer Science Direct November 2016

48 *Distinctive spring shortwave cloud radiative effect and its inter-annual variation over southeastern China* Jiandong Li, Qinglong You and Bian He 13 April 2020

49 *Cloud cover changes driven by atmospheric circulation in Europe during the last decades* Sfica, Beck, Nita, Voiculescu, Biran, Philipp 18 September 2020

50 *The West Intends Energy Suicide: Will It Succeed?* Forbes 10 October 2020

51 *Wall Street Journal* 28 September 2020

52 https://edition.cnn.com/2020/09/16/business/net-zero-climate-energy-transitions-commission/index.html

53 *The Hidden Cost of Net Zero The Spectator* 8 March 2021

54 *Guardian* 15 March 2021

55 *Guardian* 12 November 2020

56 *BBC Bitesize* 5 April 2021

57 https://www.renewablesfirst.co.uk/hydropower/hydropower-learning-centre/what-would-the-return-on-investment-be/attachment/electrictyprices-3/

58 https://www.mrt.com/business/energy/article/Spanish-study-finds-2-2-jobs-destroyed-for-each-7481656.php

59 *Biofuels turn out to be a climate mistake* The Conversation 5 October 2016

60 https://upload.wikimedia.org/wikipedia/commons/5/54/FAO_Food_Price_Index_1990-2015.png

61 IPCC Fifth Assessment Report 2013

62 From 'Donald where's yer troosers' Andy Stewart

63 Energy Central 25 February 2014

64 *The Race to Zero* The *Guardian* 15 March 2021

65 International Energy Agency 2020 report

66 https://www.researchgate.net/figure/Average-UK-household-electricity-demand-against-time-of-day-for-weekdays-and-weekends-in_fig9_324141791

Printed in Great Britain
by Amazon

20422991R00203